COLLECTING JAPANESE
MOVIE MONSTERS

COLLECTING JAPANESE
MOVIE MONSTERS

BY DANA CAIN

Radioactively Yours,
Dana Cain

ANTIQUE TRADER BOOKS

A DIVISION OF LANDMARK SPECIALTY PUBLICATIONS

NORFOLK, VIRGINIA

ISBN: 0-930625-55-2
Library of Congress Catalog Card Number: 98-89044

Editor: Wendy Chia-Klesch
Graphic Designer: Chris Decker
Copy Editor: Sandra Holcombe

Printed in the United States of America

To order additional copies of this book, or to obtain a catalog, please contact:

Antique Trader Books
P.O. Box 1050
Dubuque, Iowa 52004
1-800-334-7165
www.collect.com

TABLE OF CONTENTS

ACKNOWLEDGEMENTS

Atomic Antiques • Denver, Colorado
Robert Biondi • Brooklyn, New York
Erik Boschert • St. Charles, Missouri
Brian • G-Con highlight
Al Carr • Perth Amboy, New Jersey
The Comic Store • Westminster, Colorado
Club Daikaiju • Fort Lee, New Jersey
Kent Cordray • Denver, Colorado
Creature Feature Productions • Cambridge, Massachusetts
Diaper Man (John) • somewhere in New Jersey
Stuart Galbraith IV • Hollywood, California
Laura Givens • Denver, Colorado
J.D. Lees • Steinbach, Manitoba
Jan Lindenberger • Colorado Springs, Colorado
Sean Linkenback • Atlanta, Georgia
Nick Mancini • South Amboy, New Jersey
The Outer Limits • Clifton, New Jersey
John Rocco Roberto • Brooklyn, New York
Showcase Collectibles • Atlanta, Georgia
Nicole Spencer • Denver, Colorado
Mark ("That WaCkY Gamera Guy") Suggs • Denver, Colorado
Trendmasters • St. Louis, Missouri
Winterwolf (Bandai collection) • Aurora, Colorado
Jolyon Yates (collection and translation help) • Denver, Colorado

**And a Special Big Thanks to Thea Hutcheson of Sheridan, Colorado,
for invaluable assistance and warm friendship on the road to G-Con and back!**

THE HISTORY OF GODZILLA IN TOHO FILMS

Godzilla was first discovered on Odo Island in 1954, where a team of reporters and scientists were investigating mysterious attacks on nearby fishing vessels. The natives insisted the attacks were caused by the legendary beast, Gojira (Godzilla). Soon, the giant radioactive monster showed himself, and he's been dubbed "King of the Monsters" ever since.

The original 1954 film, *Gojira*, was a huge success in Japan, putting Toho International on the cinematic map. Two years later, it was released in the United States, with footage of Raymond Burr spliced in as a guaranteed box office draw. The film, dubbed *Godzilla, King of the Monsters,* was a huge hit in America, as well, and the stage was set for the decades of sequels that would follow.

Godzilla's initial appearance on film and in downtown Tokyo was created in the wake of the devastating bombing of Hiroshima. An allegory of radioactive destruction, Godzilla packed quite a dramatic wallop with audiences around the world.

Standing a full 164 feet tall (he got bigger in the 1980s), Godzilla was capable of the type of destruction never before seen on film. Not only did he stomp and chomp on an unprecedented scale, he was also armed with a fiery radioactive breath ray. And he seemed as indestructible as he was destructive. No weapons could pierce his thick hide. This was a very serious monster.

His first film concludes in an austere fashion, when the giant monster is dissolved by an "oxygen destroyer," deployed underwater by scientist Professor Sarazawa.

It seemed that was the end of Godzilla. But, as we know now, it was only the beginning. The following year, the monster was revived in *Godzilla's Counterattack.* Apparently, although one Godzilla had been destroyed, another monster of the same type had been found! Only this time, the monster was found battling a different monster! Godzilla's first foe, Angilas, makes his debut.

Released in America as *Gigantis the Fire Monster* (so as to avoid confusion with the first movie), this one introduced the monster fights that would become the bread and butter of the series. And this time, the director was clever enough not to kill off the star at the end. Instead, Godzilla is buried beneath a thick avalanche of snow on a remote mountainside. Gee, I wonder if he'll ever get out of that!

He does! And in 1963, Godzilla's popularity goes officially through the roof, when he's pitted against the former

King of the Monsters, King Kong. Playing up on the East vs. West theme, Toho's publicity whips audiences into a frenzy, and ***King Kong vs. Godzilla*** is a huge hit in Japan and the U.S. Toho's Kong is much bigger than the 1939 RKO ape. Toho's Kong also feeds on electricity. Let's face it—Godzilla would have snuffed the old RKO Willis O'Brien Kong in the first frame—liberties had to be taken.

As an added attempt to level the odds, scientists announce that Godzilla's brain is much smaller than Kong's. In fact, they deduce, Godzilla's brain is only the size of a marble! Considering that Godzilla is over 150 feet tall, we hope they meant a shooter.

Perhaps, in the end, it was the diminutive brain capacity that lead to Godzilla's defeat at the hands of King Kong. Rumors that the original Japanese version featured a different ending, with Godzilla as the victor, were exaggerated. In fact, the film ends with Godzilla mysteriously submerged underwater, in "apparent" defeat, while King Kong swims homeward, out to sea.

Godzilla's next foe was Mothra, the giant Moth created by Toho in its 1961 self-titled feature film. The 1964 movie, ***Godzilla vs. the Thing (Godzilla vs. Mothra)***

marked the first time Toho brought one of its existing monsters into the Godzilla universe. (Later, it would do the same with Rodan, Varan, Manda, and Moguera.) In this film, a giant egg washes ashore in the wake of a hurricane, and is soon whisked away by scientists. Godzilla, meanwhile, rises from the sea, set on destroying the implied threat. The Japanese soon team up with Mothra to thwart Godzilla's attempts to fry the egg. Alas, however, the giant moth is destroyed protecting her young, when Godzilla blasts her with his radioactive breath.

The egg, however, begins acting suspiciously, and suddenly a PAIR of Mothra larvae emerge. The little guys come out fighting, and, despite the fact that they're newborns, they give Godzilla a real run for his money, wrapping him in cocoons and eventually forcing him out to sea.

In 1965, something quite unexpected happened to Godzilla. He became a good guy.

Children who'd been following the film series had begun to take a shine to the evil destructive monster, and Toho finally decided, "Okay, we'll go with that." So, in his next film, ***Ghidrah, the Three-Headed Monster***, Godzilla is nudged into the role of Hero Monster, protecting the earth

dered into our solar system. Earth decides to loan out Godzilla and Rodan to help the new neighbors, and the two monsters are transported through space to Planet X. But, guess what! It was all an evil, evil alien trick! The aliens had been controlling Ghidrah all along, and now they had control of Godzilla and Rodan, too! Their mission—of course—was to take over earth, specifically to gain access to its water supply.

This film marks the first of many times when Godzilla falls under alien mind control. All three monsters commence a fierce, unified attack on earth. All seems lost, in fact, until someone figures out how to deprogram Godzilla and Rodan. Once back to their old selves, the two earth monsters trounce Ghidrah and send the aliens packing.

All of the films up to this point (with the notable exception of Gigantis), were directed by Ishiro Honda. That was about to change, along with Godzilla's entire demeanor. In 1966, Jun Fukuda took over the directorial reigns of Godzilla, with his first feature, *Godzilla vs. the Sea Monster.*

Seeing that Godzilla's transformation to a "good guy" was a huge success, Toho now took the formula a step further, with this film, the first of a new string of Godzilla features aimed even more fiercely toward the juvenile market.

The Sea Monster in question is Ebirah, a gigantic shrimp guarding an island where illegal slave activities and plans for world domination are ongoing. When a young girl from Mothra's homeland, Infant Island, is kidnapped and taken there, Mothra flies off to save the day. Godzilla is also on hand, and the two of them manage to defeat the cruel crustacean.

Fukuda's next outing, *Son of Godzilla*, introduced Minya, a pleasant (if not huge) toddler, learning to make his way in the world under the tender tutelage of his proud father. He must contend with gigantic insect monsters (Spiga the spider and Kamikaris, similar to a praying mantis). Minya would return in two more features before being revamped decades later as "Baby Godzilla."

Minya shows up the following year, in fact, in *Destroy All Monsters*. Actually, EVERYONE shows up in *Destroy All Monsters*, one of Toho's grandest monster epics ever. The movie features Godzilla, Rodan, Mothra, Ghidrah, Minya, Angilas, Baragon, Varan, Gorosaurus, Spiga, and Manda (from Atragon). Once again, the monsters of earth are under alien control, and each one is assigned a different section of earth to destroy. Eventually, the earth people realize the monster control transmitter is set up on the moon, and they promptly send astronauts to deactivate the evil device. Once that's done, the earth monsters settle right down. However, there is still the matter of Ghidrah,

from Villain Monsters. It was a transition that would have historical impact, forever changing Godzilla's reputation.

Ghidrah, it seems, was an alien creature of pure evil, a planet destroyer, who'd selected earth as his next picnic ground. Shooting high voltage energy beams from his three mouths, the creature begins leveling Tokyo.

Meanwhile, Godzilla and Rodan (revived after his earlier solo film) appear back on the scene and begin a fierce battle miles away from Ghidrah's reign of terror. Everywhere is destruction!

Finally, in a desperate effort to save Japan, Mothra decides (with the aid of her two tiny sidekicks, the Peanut Sisters), to try to reconcile Godzilla and Rodan in order to form a threesome to battle Ghidrah. It's not easy, but the plucky and noble little larva manages to unite the three against the common enemy, who eventually retreats back into outer space.

Ghidrah was incredibly popular, and Toho rushed him back out for an encore the following year, in *Monster Zero (Invasion of Astro-Monster).* It seems Ghidrah is harassing another planet—Planet X—which has mysteriously wan-

who goes on a lone rampage of terrifying proportions. The other monsters team together to defeat Ghidrah, however, in a blow-out finale fight staged near Mt. Fuji.

Godzilla's Revenge, released in 1969, is Fukuda's deepest plunge into childhood fantasy. The film is about a young Japanese boy, plagued by bullies, who fantasizes about his imaginary friends on Monster Island. In his mind, the boy envisions young Minya pestered by his own bully—the cruel Gabara. Eventually, as Godzilla coaches his young son to defend himself (at first Minya can only blow radioactive smoke rings), the young human hero also gains confidence. In the end, all the bullies are trounced and the good kids win.

In 1971, Jun Fukuda's directorial reign was briefly interrupted for a Godzilla film that delivered significant social and political messages. *Godzilla vs. the Smog Monster,* directed by Yoshimitsu Banno, stands out like a surrealistic social beacon in the midst of Fukuda's child-like series entries. The Smog Monster, Hedorah, is the spawn of toxic waste, evolving through several stages as an allegory for water pollution, air pollution, and land-based pollution. Memorable moments in the film include the Discotheque scene where the patrons, dancing in strobe lighting, all

have giant fish heads; the tiny kitten dying on the stairs after being "sludged" by Hedorah, and the child's poem: "Godzilla would rage if he could see/He'd save the earth for you and me."

Which, of course, he does. He also, by the way, debuts a new talent—flying—via use of his atomic breath as a propulsion system.

The next year, social commentary and parenting tips seem to be themes of the past, as Toho releases *Godzilla vs. Gigan* (*Godzilla on Monster Island* to us Americans.) It's the first of the classic monster tag team battles! In one corner—Godzilla and his little buddy, Angilas, fresh from Monster Island and now with SPEAKING parts! In the other corner—Ghidrah and the newcomer, Gigan, both under alien control! Much of the action takes place in an amusement park, around a gigantic Godzilla-shaped tower.

Gigan doesn't catch on too quickly. After he's thrashed by Godzilla once, he returns in 1973, teamed up with ANOTHER monster under alien control, Megalon! Megalon, looking much like a giant mutant cockroach with drill bits for arms, proves to be no better a fighting partner than Ghidrah had been, as he and Gigan go up against Godzilla and his new ally, Jet-Jaguar in *Godzilla vs. Megalon.* Jet-Jaguar, originally created by evil alien scientists, quickly defects to team with Godzilla and defeat the two cyborg-like space monsters.

In 1974, Toho introduced MechaGodzilla, who would become a classic in the studio's monster stable. In his first feature, *Godzilla vs. MechaGodzilla,* the giant bionic monster is sent to take over earth by space aliens. He is, originally, an exact duplicate of Godzilla, and when he begins plundering Tokyo, the locals are mightily confused, as by now everyone knows Godzilla is Tokyo's friend. Why the attack? It's all straightened out when the REAL Godzilla shows up to battle the impostor. As Godzilla blasts his atomic breath on the intruder, its skin begins to fall away, until only the metallic skeleton remains. It's a fake robot Godzilla from outer space!

Godzilla defeats MechaGodzilla with the aid of King Seesar, a mythical Japanese protector resembling a sort of floppy-eared lion. MechaGodzilla's tag team partner is the spiky little Angilas, but the pair ultimately lose.

MechaGodzilla is back the next year, however, as Toho prepares to wrap up the Godzilla film series. Ishiro Honda is called back in to direct *The Terror of MechaGodzilla.* This time, aliens find the lifeless remains of MechaGodzilla, and convince a crazy scientist to reconstruct the monster. They also manipulate the thoughts of Titanosaurus, a usually passive dinosaur, and unleash the deadly duo on earth. The aliens have MechaGodzilla and Titanosaurus on their side. But we have Godzilla. Guess who wins.

Godzilla was quiet for nine years after that. We can only assume he was lounging happily on Monster Island with his buddies. But, when he decided to come back out of retirement, he was a changed monster.

In 1984, Toho released a new *Godzilla* film, a remake of the original 1954 movie. In America, new footage was added and the movie, *Godzilla 1985*, was dubbed a sequel rather than a remake of the original. Once again, Raymond Burr plays reporter Steve Martin.

The film accomplished its mission—to remind everyone of what Godzilla was meant to be—a monster.

It was so successful, Toho decided to revive the Godzilla film series, with high-tech visual effects and a much more serious tone than had been seen in the late 1960s and the early 1970s.

In 1989, the studio began seriously producing the new string of Godzilla movies, starting with *Godzilla vs. Biollante*. The story, pulled from a massive scriptwriting contest, features a new kind of Godzilla foe. Biollante (composed partially of DNA from a rose, Godzilla, and a young girl) grows from a beautiful flowering monster into a gigantic formidable beast, equipped with several vine-like choking tentacles with mouths on the ends. Godzilla and Biollante are now both considered threats to Tokyo, and by film's end, they both have been battered by the fight and fled; Godzilla disappearing into the icy sea and Biollante scattering to seed in space.

Godzilla's next foe is a monster straight out of the classic Toho archives, Ghidrah. In *Godzilla vs. King Ghidorah* (1991), people from the future tell the Japanese that Godzilla's going to destroy Japan in the twenty-third century. They carry out a plan to prevent it by traveling back to World War II and moving the body of Godzillasaurus before it is revived and mutated by the fateful atomic blast that created Godzilla. Mission accomplished, they split, leaving behind three adorable, winged creatures called Dorats. The Dorats, however, do not stay adorable. In fact, they become King Ghidorah, and suddenly we realize the plot to prevent the creation of Godzilla was a trick to allow King Ghidorah to squash the Japanese before they become a twenty-third century super power!

In retaliation, the Japanese find the relocated body of Godzillasaurus, exposing it to a mighty dose of radiation, creating an even bigger and stronger Godzilla than ever before! He's good at fighting King Ghidorah, but also a little too good at trashing Tokyo. When Godzilla rips off Ghidorah's middle head, the humans manage to salvage the crippled monster and rebuild him with cyborg parts, adding a powerful new robotic central head, solar panel wings, and putting him under their control.

Using the new Mecha King Ghidorah, the Japanese manage to subdue Godzilla and drop him and the cyborg Ghidorah into a deep ocean trench.

Godzilla is revived the following year, however, when a meteor hits near his watery resting place. The commotion also rouses Mothra and her long lost evil twin, Battra, and *Godzilla vs. Queen Mothra* is off and running. Originally on screen as larvae, Mothra and Battra later emerge from cocoons in adult form and begin fighting over Tokyo. Godzilla, meanwhile, is wrecking Tokyo on foot. Not a good time to live in Tokyo.

Eventually, Mothra and Battra team up against Godzilla, until, finally, Mothra deems both monsters too unpredictable and winds up sealing both Godzilla and Battra under the sea.

In 1993, Toho revived and revamped MechaGodzilla, Rodan, and Minya for Godzilla vs. MechaGodzilla. Mecha-Godzilla is now a powerful robotic machine created by the Japanese to battle Godzilla. Rodan is now Fire Rodan (able to shoot energy beams) and Minya is now Baby Godzilla. Initially, Godzilla and Rodan are competing over an egg, believed to be Rodan's. When it hatches, however, the offspring is decidedly Godzillian.

While Godzilla and Rodan engage in fierce battles with MechaGodzilla, it is Rodan who makes the supreme sacrifice, giving up his life to reunite Godzilla with his son and infuse Godzilla with enough strength to defeat MechaGodzilla.

Baby Godzilla returns in 1995's *Godzilla vs. Space Godzilla*, although the little tike is now known as Little Godzilla, and his look echoes the Japanese animation style, with big, big eyes. In stark contrast to Little Godzilla's cuteness is the menacing form of Space Godzilla, the product of mutated Godzilla cells that have been sucked into a black hole and spit out again (sort of). Space Godzilla sports two gigantic crystalline shoulder pads and draws energy from an underground power structure. He seems to really have it in for Little Godzilla, so right away, he's unpopular with everyone, especially Godzilla.

Seeing the double threat of Space Godzilla and Godzilla, the Japanese deploy MOGUERA, last seen in 1957's The Mysterians. Now, MOGUERA (Mobile Operation Godzilla Universal Expert Robot Aero-type) is a tool of the United Nations Godzilla Countermeasure center. Its assignment—to destroy Space Godzilla first, and regular Godzilla second. He's fairly effective, and winds up teaming with Godzilla against Space Godzilla. But, in the end, Godzilla kills Space Godzilla, Space Godzilla kills MOGUERA and Godzilla and Little Godzilla swim away.

Godzilla's final Toho film, **Godzilla vs. Destroyah**, was released in December 1995. The film is an emotional experience for anyone who has followed the King of the Monsters for many years. It's the film where Godzilla dies.

As the movie opens, we see that Godzilla looks different. He's glowing, somehow, steaming, and scientists report he is, in fact, suffering an internal meltdown, having lost control of his own radioactive core as sort of a battle wound. The danger is that Godzilla could essentially "go up" at any minute, and when he does, everything remotely close to him is toast. If he's in Japan, Japan will be wiped off the face of the earth.

Meanwhile, another threat is growing. Destroyah—created by a mutated species of crustacean as a result of the oxygen destroyer that first killed Godzilla in 1954—is attacking Tokyo. First, he takes the form of loads of little crab-like creatures. But they keep getting bigger, and by they time they morph together, Godzilla and Tokyo are faced with one big, big monster.

Godzilla takes on the foe, but he's not feeling or fighting up to par. In fact, he's dying. Fighting valiantly at his father's side is Godzilla, Jr., and the two make a touching team. Godzilla Jr., last seen as a cutesy, big-eyed toddler in Space Godzilla, is now a formidable teen, beginning to closely resemble his father, only with smaller spines.

Godzilla Jr. stands up to Destroyah fearlessly, but is easily defeated, as the much bigger monster knocks him out, airlifts him to a nuclear power plant and drops him on it from a great height.

Godzilla, witness to this event, is heartbroken and enraged, and, in a final burst of strength, he hits Destroyah with a mighty atomic breath.

At last, Godzilla's meltdown hits the critical stage. Radioactive light beams pierce through his skin, and he begins to disintegrate. The Japanese brace for destruction and then notice the radiation is somehow being contained. A giant roar is heard, and we see Godzilla Jr. soaking up his father's discharged energy, coming back to life and growing stronger and more and more like his father.

Is the Toho Godzilla really dead?

Maybe not!

JAPANESE MONSTER MOVIES
A CHRONOLOGY

1954 - GODZILLA, KING OF THE MONSTERS, TOHO
Alternate Title: *Gojira* (original Japanese title)
U.S. Release Date: 1956
Monster Featured: Godzilla

1955 - GODZILLA'S COUNTERATTACK, TOHO
Alternate Titles: *Gigantis the Fire Monster, Godzilla Raids Again*
U.S. Release Date: 1959
Monsters Featured: Godzilla (called Gigantis this time), Angilas

1956 - RODAN, TOHO
Alternate Title: *Rodan the Flying Monster*
U.S. Release Date: 1957
Monsters Featured: Rodan and Mrs. Rodan

1957 - THE MYSTERIANS, TOHO
U.S. Release Date: 1959
Monster Featured: Moguera

1958 - VARAN THE UNBELIEVABLE, TOHO
U.S. Release Date: 1962
Monster Featured: Varan

1961 - MOTHRA (MOSURA), TOHO
U.S. Release Date: 1962
Monster Featured: Mothra

1963 - MATANGO, FUNGUS OF TERROR, TOHO
Alternate Titles: *Attack of the Mushroom People, Matango*
Monsters Featured: Matango, Mushroom People

1963 - KING KONG VS. GODZILLA, TOHO
U.S. Release Date: 1964
Monsters Featured: Godzilla, King Kong

1964 - GODZILLA VS. THE THING, TOHO
Alternate Title: *Godzilla vs. Mothra*
U.S. Release Date: 1964
Monsters Featured: Godzilla, Mothra

1964 - ATRAGON, TOHO
Monster Featured: Manda

1964 - DOGORA, THE SPACE MONSTER, TOHO
Monster Featured: Dogora

1965 - GHIDRAH, THE THREE-HEADED MONSTER, TOHO
U.S. Release Date: 1965
Monsters Featured: Ghidrah, Godzilla, Mothra, Rodan

1965 - INVASION OF ASTRO-MONSTER, TOHO

Alternate Titles: *Monster Zero, Godzilla vs. Monster Zero*
U.S. Release Date: 1970
Monsters Featured: Ghidrah, Godzilla, Rodan

1965 - FRANKENSTEIN CONQUERS THE WORLD, TOHO

Monsters Featured: Frankenstein, Baragon

1966 - GODZILLA VS. THE SEA MONSTER, TOHO

Alternate Title: *Ebirah, Horror of the Deep*
U.S. Release Date: 1968 (on TV)
Monsters Featured: Ebirah, Godzilla, Mothra

1966 - GAMERA, THE INVINCIBLE, DAIEI

U.S. Release Date: 1966
Monster Featured: Gamera

1966 - GAMERA VS. BARUGON, DAIEI

U.S. Release Date: 1966
Monsters Featured: Gamera, Barugon

1966 - WAR OF THE GARGANTUAS, TOHO

U.S. Release Date: 1966
Monsters Featured: Frankenstein and his evil twin

1967 - SON OF GODZILLA, TOHO

U.S. Release Date: 1969 (on TV)
Monsters Featured: Minya, Godzilla, Spiga, Kamakiras

1967 - GAMERA VS. GAOS, DAIEI

U.S. Release: TV only
Monsters Featured: Gamera, Gaos

1967 - KING KONG ESCAPES, TOHO

Monsters Featured: King Kong, MechaniKong

1968 - DESTROY ALL MONSTERS, TOHO

U.S. Release Date: 1969
Monsters Featured: Godzilla, Ghidrah, Rodan, Mothra, Minya, Baragon, Manda, Angilas, Varan, Spiga, Gorosaurus

1968 - GAMERA VS. VIRAS, DAIEI

U.S. Release: TV only
Monsters Featured: Gamera, Viras

1969 - GODZILLA'S REVENGE, TOHO

Alternate Title: *All Monsters Attack*
U.S. Release Date: 1971
Monsters Featured: Godzilla, Minya, Gabara, Spiga, Kamakiras, Gorosaurus, Angilas, Manda, Ebirah

1969 - GAMERA VS. GUIRON, DAIEI

U.S. Release: TV only
Monsters Featured: Gamera, Guiron

1970 - GAMERA VS. JIGER, DAIEI

U.S. Release: TV only
Monsters Featured: Gamera, Jiger

1970 - YOG! MONSTER FROM SPACE, TOHO

Monster Featured: Yog

1971 - GODZILLA VS. THE SMOG MONSTER

Alternate Title: *Godzilla vs. Hedorah*
U.S. Release Date: 1972
Monsters Featured: Godzilla, Hedorah

1971 - GAMERA VS. ZIGRA, DAIEI

Monsters Featured: Gamera, Zigra

1972 - GODZILLA VS. GIGAN, TOHO

Alternate Title: *Godzilla on Monster Island*
U.S. Release Date: 1977
Monsters Featured: Godzilla, Gigan, Angilas, Ghidrah

1973 - GODZILLA VS. MEGALON, TOHO

U.S. Release Date: 1976
Monsters Featured: Godzilla, Megalon, Jet-Jaguar, Gigan

1974 - GODZILLA VS. MECHAGODZILLA, TOHO

Alternate Titles: *Godzilla vs. the Bionic Monsters, Godzilla vs. the Cosmic Monster*
U.S. Release Date: 1976
Monsters Featured: Godzilla, MechaGodzilla, Angilas, King Seesar

1975 - *TERROR OF MECHAGODZILLA*, TOHO
Alternate Title: *Terror of Godzilla*
U.S. Release Date: 1977
Monsters Featured: Godzilla, MechaGodzilla, Titanosaurus

1984 - *GODZILLA 1984*, TOHO
Alternate Title: *Godzilla 1985* (U.S. version)
U.S. Release Date: 1985
Monster Featured: Godzilla

1989 - *GODZILLA VS. BIOLLANTE*, TOHO
Monsters Featured: Godzilla, Biollante

1991 - *GODZILLA VS. KING GHIDORAH*, TOHO
Monsters Featured: Godzilla, King Ghidorah,
    Godzillasaurus, Mecha King Ghidorah

1992 - *GODZILLA VS. MOTHRA*, TOHO
Alternate Title: *Godzilla vs. Queen Mothra*
Monsters Featured: Godzilla, Mothra, Battra

1993 - *GODZILLA VS. MECHAGODZILLA*, TOHO
Alternate Title: *Godzilla vs. MechaGodzilla II*
Monsters Featured: Godzilla, MechaGodzilla, Super
    MechaGodzilla, Baby Godzilla, Rodan, Fire Rodan

1994 - *GODZILLA VS. SPACE GODZILLA*, TOHO
Monsters Featured: Godzilla, Space Godzilla, Little
    Godzilla, Moguera, Fairy Mothra

1995 - *GODZILLA VS. DESTROYAH*, TOHO
Monsters Featured: Godzilla, Godzilla Jr., Destroyah

1995 - *GAMERA, GUARDIAN OF THE UNIVERSE*, DAIEI
Monsters Featured: Gamera, Gaos

1996 - *GAMERA 2*, DAIEI
Alternate Title: *Gamera vs. Legion*
Monsters Featured: Gamera, Legion

1997 - *MOTHRA*, TOHO
Monster Featured: Mothra

JAPANESE MOVIE
MONSTER GUIDE
(FROM ANGILAS TO ZIGRA)

ANGILAS (ANGUIRUS, ANGURUS)

Angilas was Godzilla's first foe (*Gigantis the Fire Monster*, U.S., *Godzilla Raids Again*) and he has been in five of his movies.

When Angilas first appeared in 1955's *Gigantis the Fire Monster*, he was battling Godzilla (dubbed Gigantis for this film) on a remote Pacific island. The two monsters had apparently been born in the prehistoric age of fire, and resembled two different species of dinosaurs (the Tyrannosaur and Ankylosaur). Long ago, the two had been engulfed in volcanic flame and taken deep underground, where they'd lived and fought for centuries and centuries, as fire monsters. Over the years, the ancient beasts grew and mutated, becoming more powerful and indestructible.

The advent of the Atomic Bomb freed the monsters from their underground home, unleashing them on the earth's surface—specifically Japan.

Godzilla (Gigantis) kills Angilas in their first encounter, but the spiky scrapper manages to make a death-defying comeback, appearing in four more films (*Destroy All Monsters, Godzilla's Revenge, Godzilla on Monster Island (Godzilla vs. Gigan)* and *Godzilla vs. the Cosmic (Bionic) Monster (Godzilla vs. MechaGodzilla)*. More often than not, he fights at Godzilla's side, as a short but invaluable ally. With no special powers or weapons, Angilas relies on his spikes and his spunk to battle his opponents.

Appeared in *Gigantis the Fire Monster, Destroy All Monsters, Godzilla's Revenge, Godzilla on Monster Island, Godzilla vs. the Cosmic (Bionic) Monster.*

BARAGON

Baragon debuted in 1965's *Frankenstein Conquers the World*, where he was promptly thrashed by the gigantic human monster. He was later found living on Monster Island, and in *Destroy All Monsters*, Baragon and Gorosaurus were assigned to destroy Paris.

Baragon is definitely a finalist in the "Cutest Monster" competition, and wins the "Best Ears" category hands down.

Appeared in *Frankenstein Conquers the World, Destroy All Monsters.*

BARUGON

Gamera's first foe, Barugon, was introduced in 1966. Barugon can detect danger miles away by using his "Rainbow Ray," a beautiful projection from his spiky back. He is also equipped with a super-long tongue which can issue a quick-freeze mist.

A native of New Guinea, Barugon's weakness is water. His cells actually melt when exposed to the stuff. Needless to say, he doesn't like rainy days, and, eventually, Gamera was able to drown him.

Appeared in *Gamera vs. Barugon, Space Monster Gamera.*

BATTRA

Battra is not, as its name implies, a member of the bat family. Battra is actually a darker version of Mothra, who has long been among the most sympathetic of Japanese monsters. Mothra is forced to do battle with her shadow side, until the two unite against Godzilla. The action takes place in 1992's *Godzilla vs. Queen Mothra.*

Battra first appears as a tough, spiked caterpillar, released from the polar ice cap. In addition to spouting cocoon-spray, Battra can also emit powerful energy beams from its eyes and its rhino-like front horn. After being engulfed in an underwater eruption, Battra re-emerges as a beautiful, dark moth, with a mission. Battra is actually an ally of earth, dedicated to fighting for the safety of the earth and its ecosystem at all costs. When Godzilla is identified as a severe ecological threat, our favorite monster becomes Battra's prime target.

Eventually, Mothra decides that both Godzilla and her driven twin are a bit too ruthless to remain at large in the world, and she seals both of them underwater. So much for sisterly love.

Appeared in *Godzilla vs. Queen Mothra* (1992).

BIOLLANTE

Biollante is more than just an angry rose bush.

Actually, it was created by a well-meaning geneticist, who combined the DNA of his dead daughter, a rose petal, and Godzilla. What was he thinking?

Initially, Biollante rose from the water as a gigantic plundering botanical atrocity. That got the attention of Godzilla, who promptly freed himself from a nearby volcano and went to defend his stomping grounds.

Once exposed to Godzilla's radioactive breath ray, however, Biollante mutates into a more formidable opponent. Already partially composed of Godzilla material, the flowering foe begins to more resemble the attacking "parent." Only bigger. And with more mouths.

Biollante in its final form, is an awe-inspiring mixture of plant and animal ferocity. In addition to its main head, it has four choking vine-like tentacles, each equipped with a powerful, sharp-toothed mouth. And, if that's not enough, the monster also emits an acid-like, radioactive sap, which it can spray at will.

Eventually, of course, Biollante submits to its final pruning by the mightiest monster, Godzilla. Last seen, Biollante scatters to seed, floats into space, and is immortalized as a beautiful rose orbiting the earth.

Appeared in *Godzilla vs. Biollante*.

DESTROYAH (DESTROYER)

Godzilla's final foe (future TriStar releases notwithstanding), Destroyah, is, perhaps, the most despised of all Toho monsters. This creature is merciless, and, unlike most of Toho's monsters, has absolutely no redeeming characteristics.

His origin is traced back to the deployment of the oxygen destroyer, used to kill Godzilla way back in the 1950s. That devastating weapon revived and mutated a colony of tiny Precambrian crustaceans. So, Destroyah first appears as an army of like-minded crab-like creatures, which proceed to grow in size until they finally merge into one huge hardshelled monster. From there, they morph into a flying

Baragon

beast, and finally, settle into the mature form of a gigantic winged, two-footed, horned monster.

What makes Destroyah even more despicable than usual is that he almost kills Godzilla's son, Godzilla Jr. The father is visibly shaken, and, unfortunately, never lives to see that his son is still alive.

Appeared in *Godzilla vs. Destroyah*.

EBIRAH

Although Ebirah closely resembles a giant lobster, his name is actually derived from the Japanese "Ebi," meaning "shrimp." But, rest assured, this is a JUMBO shrimp.

Introduced in 1966's ***Godzilla vs. the Sea Monster (Ebirah, Horror of the Deep)***, Ebirah was the guard shrimp for an evil slave labor base being run off a remote South Pacific island by a group called the Red Bamboo. His job was to keep slaves from escaping, and keep anyone from interfering with the island and its secret activities. He did a great job, too, until Godzilla and Mothra came along. Ebirah was summarily declawed and dismissed, only to reappear a few years later in Godzilla's Revenge.

Appeared in *Godzilla vs. the Sea Monster, Godzilla's Revenge.*

Gamera

FRANKENSTEIN

Toho's Frankenstein bears only the slightest resemblance to his more famous American-made Universal Studios counterpart. The monster is born when the heart of the original Frankenstein monster is transported to Hiroshima by Nazis, and inexplicably eaten by a little boy right after the atomic bomb is dropped. The kid grows to gigantic proportions and takes up residence in the country, where he is forced to battle Baragon.

In his second feature, **War of the Gargantuas**, Frankenstein loses an arm, which grows into an evil twin. The two battle it out until they are both trapped (forever?) inside a volcano.

Appeared in *Frankenstein Conquers the World, War of the Gargantuas*.

GABARA

Gabara was the bully on Monster Island who terrorized Godzilla's son, Minya, in the imaginative fantasy, **Godzilla's Revenge**. Able to shoot bolts of electricity from his arms and his rhino-like horn, Gabara was finally trounced by Godzilla.

Appeared in *Godzilla's Revenge*.

GAMERA

Gamera, a giant prehistoric turtle, was awakened by atomic blasting in 1965; Daiei Studio's reaction to the popularity of Toho's Godzilla films. Gamera fought many foes throughout the late 1960s until 1971, when he vanished (making only a half-baked comeback in 1979's **Space Monster Gamera**, a stock footage nightmare).

After Toho revived Godzilla in the late 1980s and 1990s, Daiei produced **Gamera, Guardian of the Universe,** featuring a somewhat more serious and muscular version of the star turtle. To the delight of Japanese monster fans, the studio is continuing to release new Gamera movies.

Appeared in *Gamera, the Invincible, Gamera vs. Barugon, Gamera vs. Gaos, Gamera vs. Viras, Gamera vs. Guiron, Gamera vs. Jiger, Gamera vs. Zigra, Gamera Super Monster, Gamera, Guardian of the Universe, Gamera II (Gamera vs. Legion)*.

GAOS (GYAOS)

Perhaps Gamera's most popular adversary, Gaos has battled the hero turtle in three films. Introduced in 1967, the bat-like creature drinks blood, eats people, and causes tornadoes with its incessant wing flapping. He can also shoot a "supersonic knife beam" from his mouth, emit fire-repellent from his chest and fly at speeds exceeding Mach 1.

Awakened from his underground slumber by a road construction crew, Gaos was defeated by Gamera in 1967, but he managed to come back in 1979 and in 1995's **Gamera, Guardian of the Universe**, causing nothing by trouble!

Appeared in *Gamera vs. Gaos, Space Monster Gamera, Gamera, Guardian of the Universe*.

GHIDRAH (GHIDORAH, KING GHIDORAH, MECHAGHIDORAH)

Ghidrah the Three-Headed Monster made his debut in 1963 in Japan (a year later in the United States), and right off the bat, went up against Godzilla, Mothra, and Rodan.

Apparently, Ghidrah was an ancient evil force, roaming the universe destroying planet after planet before he landed on earth.

More often than any other Toho monster, Ghidrah has been forced under the control of evil space aliens. Ghidrah's led a tough life, including being decapitated (just the middle head) and refurbished as a cyborg to do the bidding of humans in his final film. And not once did Ghidrah fight on Godzilla's side in a battle.

Appeared in *Ghidrah the Three-Headed Monster, Monster Zero, Destroy All Monsters, Godzilla on Monster Island (Godzilla vs. Gigan), Godzilla vs. MechaGodzilla (The Cosmic Monster), Terror of MechaGodzilla, Godzilla vs. King Ghidorah.*

GIGAN (GAIGAN, BORODAN)

Gigan, a cyborg monster sent to destroy earth by evil space aliens, has appeared in two Godzilla films. In addition to his claw-like metal arms, his most amusing weaponry is the vibrating buzz saw protruding from his belly.

Originally teamed with Ghidrah in **Godzilla vs. Gigan**, he later returned with a new ally, Megalon, to attempt an overthrow of earth. Both attempts failed, but he is still a really cool monster.

Appeared in *Godzilla on Monster Island (Godzilla vs. Gigan), Godzilla vs. Megalon.*

GODZILLA (TOHO)

Often cited as a direct reaction to the Hiroshima bombing, Godzilla was, in his original inception, a gigantic, terrifying abomination, created when radiation revived and mutated a dinosaur. As audiences demanded sequels, however, Godzilla's popularity mellowed the creature somewhat, and he became nicer . . . and nicer. His eyes got bigger, his nose got puggier. He became Japan's greatest hero, fighting off other monsters to defend his favorite stomping grounds.

In 1984, however, Toho changed all that. They released a movie portraying Godzilla once again as a serious force to be reckoned with. After the film was released in the United States as the highly modified **Godzilla 1985**, Toho decided not to ship over any of Godzilla's later films. If they had, the U.S. would have seen a new, powerful Godzilla. As it stands, those not willing to track down imported subtitled videotapes of the recent Godzilla films are left with only the happiest memories of Godzilla.

Appeared in 22 films, including all that bear his name plus *Gigantis the Fire Monster (Godzilla Raids Again), Ghidrah the Three-Headed Monster, Monster Zero, Destroy All Monsters.*

GODZILLA (TRISTAR)

A very different Godzilla, in appearance and origin, the American TriStar Godzilla was the product of French atomic testing in the South Pacific. Only in this case, (s)he was not a mutated dinosaur, but a mutated iguana, who migrates to Manhattan Island to lay eggs at Madison Square Garden.

The American Godzilla may look slightly more plausible as an actual species, with flashier muscles and a more lizard-like head, but the shock of the redesign was too much for most old school Godzilla fans.

Appeared in *Godzilla* (1998).

GODZILLASAURUS

Knowing that Godzilla was born when a nuclear accident mutated and revived a dead dinosaur after World War II, people from the future (Futurians), travel to the past to rescue the original dinosaur—Godzillasaurus—and move him to a "safer" location, away from the radiation. When the people of the present day realize that it's a trick to remove Godzilla from his stomping grounds so that the Futurians, with the aid of Ghidrah, can take over Japan, they revive Godzillasaurus with a new nuclear missile, creating an even larger, more powerful Godzilla, as seen in the Toho films of the 1990s.

Appeared in *Godzilla vs. King Ghidorah.*

Godzillasaurus

GOROSAURUS

Gorosaurus is a gigantic kangaroo-kicking dinosaur that was first discovered on Mondo Island in **King Kong Escapes**. Although he appeared to be killed by King Kong in that film, he did later guest shots in **Destroy All Monsters** (trouncing Paris) and in Godzilla's Revenge.

Appeared in *King Kong Escapes, Destroy All Monsters, All Monsters Attack*.

GUIRON

Gamera's belligerent knife-headed foe, Guiron, came to earth from Sol X in 1969. Not the brightest bulb in the monster world, Guiron makes up for his slowness (both physical and mental) by shooting "ninja stars" from his head. The fact that over half of his body is a giant knife-like protrusion emitting from his head makes him all the more formidable. Still, he was no match for Gamera.

Appeared in *Gamera vs. Guiron, Space Monster Gamera*.

HEDORAH (THE SMOG MONSTER)

"Hedorah" means, literally, "Sludge" in Japanese. This is the monster who perhaps represents Toho's most dramatic social comment. With a back-up theme song, pleading "Save the Earth," Hedorah first appears as an organized, ominous blob of water pollution, the result of a space-born seed interacting with earth's industrial waste. In the form of a tadpole swarm, Hedorah gradually merges its small units into one large creature. Flying over Tokyo, Hedorah emits a lethal spray of acid. He can also shoot deadly energy beams from his eyes and spurt toxic mud onto those who cross his path. When introduced in 1971, the Smog Monster was the flashiest monster Godzilla had ever encountered, in terms of natural weaponry. But, finally, Godzilla and his human allies managed to defeat Hedorah using high-tech electrical dehydration methods and Godzilla's big feet.

Appeared in *Godzilla vs. the Smog Monster*.

JET-JAGUAR

One of the best features of **Godzilla vs. Megalon**, Jet-Jaguar is the heroic robot who defects from the direction of evil-doers to side with Godzilla against the double threat of Megalon and Gigan. Created by the ingenious inventor, Goro Ibuki, Jet-Jaguar can change his size, growing from human proportions to Godzilla-like stature in moments. He is also able to fly, communicate with monsters, and use a variety of smooth kung fu fighting techniques.

Appeared in *Godzilla vs. Megalon*.

Hedorah

JIGER (JAIGER)

Jiger battled Gamera in 1970, and, although he couldn't defeat the hero turtle, he did manage to impregnate him! The asexual beast knocked Gamera unconscious and, with the spike in his tail, inserted an egg beneath the hero's shell. Jiger can also impale enemies with his "solid saliva spears" (yes, petrified slobber), and he can project a heat ray from the top of his head.

He is vulnerable to high-pitched noises, however, and an ancient statue called "the Devil's Whistle" (or perhaps a Yoko Ono CD) can totally immobilize him.

Appeared in *Godzilla vs. Jiger, Space Monster Gamera*.

KAMAKIRAS

This giant insect, resembling a praying mantis, appeared in three Godzilla series films. Initially, a few of these insects were exposed to radiation on their remote island home, causing them to grow to gargantuan proportions. Their food source of choice seemed to be Godzilla's offspring—not a healthy diet. In fact, Godzilla held them successfully at bay. At least one of the Kamakiras tribe, however, is still living on Monster Island.

Appeared in *Son of Godzilla, Godzilla's Revenge and Godzilla vs. Gigan (Godzilla on Monster Island)*.

KING KONG

Toho's version of the mighty King Kong has appeared in two films, once battling Godzilla, and once fighting a mechanized version of himself. Toho's Kong, inspired by the Willis O'Brien creation of 1933, is far larger than his namesake, and feeds off electricity, even to the point of shooting it from his fingertips. Discovered on the legendary Faro Island, somewhere in the South Pacific, King Kong arrives in Japan to battle Godzilla, in a fight symbolically pitting East against West.

In any country, King Kong remains one of the greatest monsters of all time.

Appeared in *King Kong vs. Godzilla, King Kong Escapes.*

KING SEESAR (KING CAESAR)

One of the "good guys," King Seesar is actually a mythological protective beast from Japanese history. Part lion, the mostly mammalian monster is summoned from his temple home to side with Godzilla against the evil MechaGodzilla.

Appeared in *Godzilla vs. the Cosmic (Bionic) Monster.*

LEGION

A relatively new thorn in Gamera's side, Legion debuted in 1996's Gamera 2. Echoing shades of Godzilla's final foe, Destroyah, Legion begins his threat as a swarm of smallish, one-eyed insectoid fiends. Eventually, however, the creatures morph into one gigantic, hard-shelled threat.

Appeared in *Gamera 2: The Advent of Legion.*

MANDA

The snake-like Manda, with a classic Oriental dragon head, joined the Godzilla series after debuting in Toho's Atragon, about a futuristic submarine. Originally employed as the guardian of the undersea kingdom of Mu, Manda, with his powerful constricting coils, is summoned to help attack Tokyo by the evil Kilaaks in **Destroy All Monsters**.

Appeared in *Atragon, Destroy All Monsters, Godzilla's Revenge, Terror of MechaGodzilla.*

MECHAGODZILLA (SUPER MECHAGODZILLA, THE COSMIC MONSTER)

MechaGodzilla was originally created by space aliens hoping to take over the earth. He debuted in 1974's **Godzilla vs. MechaGodzilla (the Cosmic Monster)** and was revived the following year in **The Terror of MechaGodzilla (Terror of Godzilla)**. About two decades later, Toho brought him back again, this time as a Japanese-built weapon against Godzilla.

MechaGodzilla becomes Super MechaGodzilla when combined with Garuda, a supercharged fighting jet.

Appeared in *Godzilla vs. the Bionic (Cosmic) Monster, The Terror of Godzilla (both Americanized titles) and Godzilla vs. MechaGodzilla.*

MECHANIKONG

Originally created as a tool to mine radioactive material from deep underground, MechaniKong eventually malfunctions, and winds up battling his mammalian counterpart in downtown Tokyo. Appearing exclusively in **King Kong Escapes,** MechaniKong's cartoony design was partially due to the fact that the film was made in conjunction with Rankin/Bass, the American company that created the 1960s King Kong cartoon show.

Appeared in *King Kong Escapes.*

MEGALON

Megalon is one of Godzilla's cyborg enemies, closely resembling a cockroach with drill bit arms. He can burrow underground at an amazing speed, and fire lightning bolts from a horn-like antenna on top of his head. Megalon was actually sent to Japan by an undersea civilization called Seatopia, to defend the oceans against nuclear testing. Gigan joined him in the fight, but the two were ultimately defeated by Godzilla and the Seatopian traitor, Jet-Jaguar.

Appeared in *Godzilla vs. Megalon.*

MechaGodzilla

MINYA (BABY GODZILLA, LITTLE GODZILLA, GODZILLA JR.)

Godzilla's offspring has changed over the years. In his earliest appearances, as the clownish Minya in *Son of Godzilla* (1967) and the infamous *Godzilla's Revenge* (1969), he was a comic figure, who could only manage to puff out a meager radioactive smoke ring when he tried to imitate dad's death breath.

Finally, in the 1990s, Toho began taking the idea of a baby Godzilla more seriously, and created—Baby Godzilla. By the time Godzilla hit his Japanese swan song, in 1995's *Godzilla vs. Destroyah*, Baby Godzilla (now Godzilla Jr.) had grown into a formidable monster in his own right. In fact, he fights valiantly at his father's side, right up to the end. The two monsters seem genuinely bonded, and at last, the audience is spared the goofy voices and the comic relief. Godzilla's son has grown up.

Appeared in *Son of Godzilla, Destroy All Monsters, Godzilla's Revenge, Godzilla vs. MechaGodzilla, Godzilla vs. Space Godzilla and Godzilla vs. Destroyah.*

Moguera

MOGUERA (MOGERA, M.O.G.U.E.R.A.)

Moguera originally appeared in *The Mysterians* (1957) as an invading robot and was revamped decades later as a weapon of G-Force in *Godzilla vs. Space Godzilla*. Moguera's name is now an acronym for Mobile Operation Godzilla Universal Expert Robot Aero-type.

The new Moguera, created to defend Tokyo against Godzilla, actually wound up teaming with him against the greater threat of Space Godzilla. Although Moguera contributed significantly to the battle, he was ultimately destroyed by the more powerful monster.

Appeared in *The Mysterians, Godzilla vs. Space Godzilla.*

MOTHRA (QUEEN MOTHRA, FAIRY MOTHRA)

Mothra has appeared in numerous films, and is almost always depicted as one of the "good" monsters. As a caterpillar, she is capable of shooting a spray of cocooning silky threads from her mouth. With telepathic ties to a pair of minute Oriental twins (known in some circles as the Peanut Sisters), Mothra was rarely seen in adult form between her 1961 debut and her 1990s resurrection.

Mothra may be the most sympathetic of all the giant Japanese monsters, always fighting for peace and the earth.

Appeared in *Mothra, Godzilla vs. the Thing, Ghidrah the Three-Headed Monster, Godzilla vs. the Sea Monster, Destroy All Monsters, Godzilla vs. Mothra, Godzilla vs. Space Godzilla (as Fairy Mothra) and Queen Mothra.*

RODAN (FIRE RODAN)

Toho's second monster film, *Rodan* (1956), is a love story. Set against a backdrop of dubbed screams and fiery devastation, it tells the story of two alienated monsters, bonded and committed to one another, who must literally fight the world for their survival. One is killed.

The other eventually moves beyond his incredible grief to star in a series of films with Godzilla. Rodan quickly becomes one of the "Good Guy" monsters, and helps Godzilla battle a bevy of hostile upstarts. His wingspan is rumored to be about 400 feet.

Rodan was resurrected in 1993's *Godzilla vs. MechaGodzilla*. This time, transformed by a harrowing battle with Godzilla, Rodan is upgraded to Fire Rodan, bigger and redder than before, and armed with a radioactive heat ray. Inexplicably determined to protect Godzilla's young, Rodan is eventually destroyed by MechaGodzilla, and, as his dying act, the giant prehistoric bird wraps his wings around Godzilla and lets all his energy flow into the dying monster, reviving him to defeat the common enemy.

Appeared in *Rodan, Ghidrah the Three-Headed Monster, Monster Zero, Destroy All Monsters, Godzilla vs. MechaGodzilla.*

SPACE GODZILLA

Space Godzilla was created when one of Godzilla's powerful "G-cells" was carried into space (either by Biollante's spores or Mothra) and was sucked into a Black Hole. The G-cell then combined with alien material, mutated, and re-emerged into this dimension as Space Godzilla. Sure . . . why not?

Space Godzilla is equipped with lots of crystalline structure, most notably two giant crystal shoulder pads capable of drawing energy from the earth and creating massive "gravity tornadoes." The monster is finally defeated when Godzilla figures out how to cut him off from his crystalline power source.

Appeared in *Godzilla vs. Space Godzilla.*

SPIGA (KUMONGA)

This giant spider is really creepy. Originally fighting against Godzilla and his son, Spiga later teamed with the two to battle Ghidrah in **Destroy All Monsters.**

Appeared in *Son of Godzilla, Destroy All Monsters, Godzilla's Revenge.*

TITANOSAURUS

Titanosaurus was a simple, mild-mannered dinosaur . . . until evil space aliens revived it and brain-washed it into teaming with MechaGodzilla against Godzilla. Combining formidable qualities of both reptile and fish, Titanosaurus looks nothing like the actual dinosaur of the same name. And, despite the dinosaur's worthy fighting prowess, it was no match for the King of the Monsters, and, eventually, beat a hasty retreat seaward.

Appeared in *The Terror of MechaGodzilla.*

VARAN

Introduced in its own self-titled feature film, Varan made a special guest appearance with the Godzilla gang in **Destroy All Monsters.** Able to walk, swim, and fly with equal aptitude, Varan is, definitely, unbelievable.

Appeared in *Varan the Unbelievable, Destroy All Monsters.*

VIRAS

Originating on the planet Viras, this remarkably-designed squid-like creature battled Gamera in 1968. Viras has three

Space Godzilla

triangular head plates which, when pulled together, form a horrid stabbing weapon. Viras can merge with others of its kind to grow from 3 meters to a full 80 meters tall (standard height for Gamera foes). He can also assume the form of a human by killing one and donning his or her body. Viras also controls a huge space craft armed with a Super Catch Ray that can immobilize prey. And, if that's not enough, Viras has mind control powers! Look out!

Appeared in *Gamera vs. Viras, Space Monster Gamera.*

ZIGRA

Bird-like in appearance, Zigra is actually a sort of space shark. He arrived on earth from the Planet Zigra in 1971, much to the dismay of Gamera, who was forced to kill him.

Zigra sports a row of knife-like fins on his back, and his pectoral fins are also quite knife-like. For those out of his reach, Zigra is armed with a "cellular disrupter beam." Ouch, that's gotta hurt.

Appeared in *Gamera vs. Zigra, Space Monster Gamera.*

A HISTORY OF COLLECTING JAPANESE
MONSTER TOYS

Japanese monster toys have been around for decades, although only one was released during the 1950s. The very first licensed Godzilla toy was a rifle, issued in Japan to coincide with Godzilla's first sequel, *Godzilla Raids Again (Gigantis the Fire Monster)* in 1955.

Eight years later, American toy manufacturers started the Godzilla marketing craze in earnest, when Ideal introduced a Godzilla board game following the success of *King Kong vs. Godzilla*. Aurora soon followed suit and released its popular Godzilla model kit. It was then that the Japanese company, Marusan, got the idea to issue a vinyl Godzilla figure based on the Aurora model. It came out in 1964, a full decade after Godzilla first wrecked Tokyo.

After the Aurora model kits, the Americans lost interest in creating Godzilla toys for a while, but the Japanese were just getting started. Marusan continued to issue vinyl toys, model kits and a few tin toys for the duration of the 1960s, before going bankrupt around 1970. Today, Marusan's toys are highly collectible, representing the first in the line of Japanese Godzilla toys. Although not very realistic, the enemy monsters command the highest prices, since fewer of them were sold originally. Godzilla himself is the easiest to find, as with most of the Japanese monster toy lines.

When Marusan went under, another Japanese company named Bullmark emerged, took over Marusan's molds, and continued to issue the tin and vinyl toys. Bullmark added a dozen or so new vinyl toys of their own, along with some die-cast metal toys in 1976-1977, which are highly sought by today's Godzilla collectors. Godzilla, the cheapest of the die-cast line, was issued in green and brown. The rarest, Angilas, was released just before Bullmark went bankrupt in 1978.

When Bullmark went bankrupt, Popy entered the Godzilla toy scene. A division of Bandai, the company produced Godzilla toys under its own name until 1983, when Bandai first began issuing the toys with its own mark. Collectors should note, however, that Godzilla toys marked "Bandai 1983" were not necessarily created during that first year of production.

Today, discontinued Bandai pieces are very collectible, and not easily found in America.

Bandai's series of Godzilla toys, based on Godzilla's final Toho film, *Godzilla vs. Destroyah*, sold well in Japan and in the U.S., despite Toho's resistance to Godzilla exports. To commemorate Godzilla's final moments, Bandai released a very limited edition figure called "Meltdown Godzilla" which was only sold at the theaters showing *Godzilla vs. Destroyah* in Japan. There were supposedly only 5,000 of the figures made, and maybe only about 1,000 made it over to the U.S.

Meltdown Godzilla is made from the same mold as the more accessible "Burning Godzilla" figure, which shows the character in the early stages of death. The limited edition figure is cast in bright red and orange translucent plastic, representing Godzilla's final fiery moments.

Much more accessible in the United States is the popular line of Trendmasters Godzilla toys. Trendmasters owner and CEO, Russell Hornsby, has been a Godzilla fan since he was a kid. With dozens of different pieces and "godzillions" of toys sold, Trendmasters is quite happy with its Godzilla license. The company managed to wrestle the American license away from Imperial, manufacturers of a few sizes of hastily executed Godzilla plastic figures between about 1985-1995.

Trendmasters' bestseller is reportedly Godzilla, himself. "Everybody likes Ghidrah, but Godzilla is still King of the Monsters. Everyone wants Godzilla first," the toy company reps say.

Today, collectors are beginning to show some interest in the Trendmasters pieces in the original "King of the Monsters packaging. Also, the non-action figure pieces from the original line (such as bendees, key chains, jump-up figures, banks, etc.) are beginning to draw some attention. But, because of the huge supply of these toys, prices have not yet increased greatly beyond the original price.

One Trendmasters tracker, however, reports that the 6-inch Biollante figure is much harder to come by than the others, having found only three Biollante figures among 480 shipped in several cases.

Since the late 1980s, Bandai and other Japanese companies have been issuing some very high ticket, high tech Godzilla toys. Billiken has produced some wonderful Godzilla and Mothra tin toys, along with their line of garage kits. Bandai has issued some amazing motorized igures, radio-controlled figures and toys that walk, roar, glow, and more.

And, for those who take Godzilla a little less seriously, there is the "Superdeformed" series. They're downright adorable, squashed into tiny proportions, inspired by Japan's animation style. In Japan, Godzilla and many other popular character toys are available in Superdeformed versions. It's a national fad, and one that many collectors have grown to love. Some Godzilla collectors, in fact, only collect the Superdeformed series.

CHAPTER ONE
JAPANESE & AMERICAN
FIGURES

AA

MULTI-MONSTER PLAYSETS

Mini Godzilla Playset, seven monsters, figures are
1.75 in. tall, AA, Japan (Figure 1-1) $8-15

BANDAI

ANGILAS · ANGUIRUS · ANGURUS

Figure, Angilas, plastic, 4 in. tall, Bandai, 1990 25-50

Figure, Angilas, Bullmark reissue 25-50

Miniature figure, Angilas, detailed gray vinyl, 1.5 in.,
marked "T.T.," Bandai, 1994 (Figure 1-2) 5-9

(Figure 1-1) Mini Godzilla Playset, AA.

(Figure 1-2) Miniature Angilas, Bandai.

BARAGON

Figure, Baragon, 7 in., Bandai, 1992
(Figure 1-3) 175-225

Figure, Baragon, orange painted plastic, 9 in.,
Bullmark reissue, Bandai, 1992 (Figure 1-4) . . . 35-50

Miniature figure, Baragon, detailed gray vinyl, 1.5 in.,
marked "T.T.," Bandai, 1994 5-9

(Figure 1-3) Baragon figure, Bandai.

(Figure 1-5) Battra Adult, Bandai.

(Figure 1-4) Baragon, Bullmark reissue, Bandai.

(Figure 1-6) Battra Larva, Bandai.

BATTRA

Figure, Battra Adult, 15-in. wingspan, with stand,
Bandai, 1992 (Figure 1-5) $50-75

Figure, Battra Larva, 5 in. tall, Bandai, 1992
(Figure 1-6) 20-40

Miniature figure, Battra, light blue vinyl, 1.5 in.,
Bandai, 1996 4-8

BIOLLANTE

Action figure, Biollante, plastic, 8 in., Bandai,
boxed, 1992 (Figure 1-7) 175-250

DESTROYAH · DESTROYER

Action figure, Destroyah, Crab Phase, plastic, 6 in.,
Bandai, 1995 (Figure 1-8) 20-40

Action figure, Destroyah, Final Phase, plastic,
9 in., Bandai, 1995 (Figure 1-9) 40-65

Glow-in-the-dark miniature figure, Destroyah,
light orange plastic, 1.5 in., Bandai, 1993 5-10

(Figure 1-7) Biollante, Bandai.

EBIRAH

Glow-in-the-dark miniature figure, Ebirah,
light orange plastic, 1.5 in., Bandai, 1993 . . . . . $5-10

GHIDRAH · GHIDORAH · KING GHIDORAH · MECHAGHIDORAH · DEATH GHIDORAH

Action figure, Death Ghidorah, 7 in., Bandai, 1996
(Figure 1-10) 35-45

Action figure, Ghidrah 1964, 9 in., Bandai, 1984
(Figure 1-11) 175-225

(Figure 1-8) Destroyah, Crab Phase, Bandai.

(Figure 1-10) Death Ghidorah, Bandai.

(Figure 1-9) Destroyah, Final Phase, Bandai.

(Figure 1-11) Ghidrah 1964, Bandai.

Action figure, Ghidrah, orange painted plastic, 10 in.,
Bullmark reissue, Bandai, 1992 (Figure 1-12). . $35-50

Action figure, Ghidrah, soft plastic, 4.5 in.,
Bandai, Big Godzilla boxed series, 1994
(Figure 1-13) 10-20

Action figure, Ghidrah, yellow painted plastic,
9 in., 1991 35-45

Action figure, MechaGhidorah, soft plastic, 4.5 in.,
Bandai, Big Godzilla boxed series, 1994 10-20

Action figure, Mecha King Ghidorah, 12 in.,
Bandai, 1991 (Figure 1-14) $125-175

Miniature figure, King Ghidorah, detailed gray vinyl,
1.5 in., marked "T.T.," Bandai, 1994 5-9

Miniature figure, Mecha King Ghidorah, detailed gray
vinyl, 1.5 in., marked "T.T.," Bandai, 1994
(Figure 1-15) 5-9

"Super-real" painted miniature figure, Mecha King
Ghidorah, 2.5 in., Bandai, 1995 6-12

(Figure 1-13) Ghidrah, 4.5 in., Bandai.

(Figure 1-14) Mecha King Ghidorah, Bandai.

(Figure 1-15) Miniature King Ghidorah, Bandai.

(Figure 1-12) Ghidrah, Bullmark reissue, Bandai.

(Figure 1-16) Gigan, Bandai.

GIGAN

Action figure, Gigan, plastic, 8 in., Bandai, 1990
(Figure 1-16) $25-50

Action figure, Gigan, black painted plastic, 8 in.,
Bandai 90-110

Figure, Gigan, painted vinyl, 9 in., Bullmark reissue,
Bandai, 1992 35-50

Miniature figure, Gigan, silver plastic, 1.5 in., Bandai,
1993 (Figure 1-17) 5-9

Translucent Superdeformed Gigan figure, from machines in Japanese theater lobbies, 1.5 in., Bandai,
1995 (shown unassembled) (Figure 1-18) 2-5

GODZILLA

Action figure, Godzilla, soft plastic, 4.5 in., Bandai,
Big Godzilla boxed series, 1994 10-20

Burning Godzilla, black and orange plastic, 9 in.,
1995 (Figure 1-19) 25-40

"Disco" Godzilla, gold glitter, 9 in., Godzilla
Forever series, 1996 (Figure 1-20) 150-250

(Figure 1-17) Miniature Gigan, Bandai.

(Figure 1-18) Super-deformed Gigan, Bandai.

(Figure 1-20) "Disco" Godzilla, Bandai.

(Figure 1-19) Burning Godzilla, Bandai.

Godzilla 1954, Bandai, 1995 (Figure 1-21) $15-30

Godzilla 1962, 9 in. 200-275

Godzilla 1964, 18 in., Bandai, 1988
(Figure 1-22) 150-250

Godzilla 1964, 8.25 in., 1983 (Figure 1-23) . . . 100-150

Godzilla 1984, 9 in. 125-200

Godzilla 1991, 8 in. (mouth closed), 1991
(Figure 1-24) 100-145

Godzilla 1991, 14 in., 1991 (Figure 1-25) $125-175

Godzilla 1992, 8 in. (open mouth) 35-50

Godzilla 1994, standard 8-9 in. size (Figure 1-26) . 35-50

Godzilla, black and silver plastic, arms move,
4.25 in., 1992 20-30

Godzilla, fuzzy, cute figure with puffy cheeks,
3.25 in., early 1980s (Figure 1-27) 20-30

Godzilla, fuzzy, cute figure with puffy cheeks,
larger promo for above, 7.5 in., early 1980
(Figure 1-28) 75-100

Godzilla, glow-in-the-dark miniature figure, light
orange plastic, 1.5 in., Bandai,
1993 (Figure 1-29) 5-10

Meltdown Godzilla, articulated translucent red
and orange plastic, ltd. ed., originally sold only in
Japanese theaters showing *Godzilla vs. Destroyah*,
9 in., 1995 (Figure 1-30) 100-300

Meltdown Godzilla, super big scale, numbered ed.,
4000 made, 1995 550-650

Melting Godzilla, red, gray, and translucent white,
9 in., Godzilla Forever series, 1996
(Figure 1-31) 75-150

(Figure 1-22) Godzilla 1964, 18 in., Bandai.

(Figure 1-29) Glow-in-the-dark miniature Godzilla, Bandai.

(Figure 1-21) Godzilla 1954, Bandai.

(Figure 1-23) Godzilla 1964, 8.25 in., Bandai.

(Figure 1-27) "Fuzzy" Godzilla, 3.25 in., Bandai.

(Figure 1-28) "Fuzzy" Godzilla, 7.5 in., Bandai.

(Figure 1-32) "Super-real" miniature Godzilla, Bandai.

(Figure 1-26) Godzilla 1994, Bandai.

(Figure 1-30) Meltdown Godzilla, from Godzilla vs. Destroyah, Bandai.

(Figure 1-31) Melting Godzilla, Bandai.

(Figure 1-24) Godzilla 1991, 8 in., Bandai.

(Figure 1-25) Godzilla 1991, 14 in., Bandai.

Miniature figure, Godzilla, detailed gray vinyl, 1.5 in., marked "T.T.," Bandai, 1994 . . . . $5-9

"Super-real" painted miniature figure, Godzilla, brown or black variant, 2.5 in., Bandai, 1995 (Figure 1-32) 6-12

Translucent Superdeformed Godzilla figure from machines in Japanese theater lobbies, 1.5 in., Bandai, 1995 2-5

GODZILLASAURUS

Action figure, Godzillasaurus, plastic, 6 in., Bandai, 1992 (Figure 1-33) $15-25

GOROSAURUS

Miniature figure, Gorosaurus, detailed gray vinyl, 1.5 in., marked "T.T.," Bandai, 1994 (Figure 1-34) 5-9

HEDORAH · SMOG MONSTER

Glow-in-the-dark miniature figure, Hedorah,
   light orange plastic, 1.5 in., Bandai,
   1993 (Figure 1-35) $5-10

Figure, Hedorah, plastic, 7 in., Bandai, 1993
   (Figure 1-36) 30-60

JET-JAGUAR

Action figure, Jet-Jaguar, plastic, Bandai 20-35

KING KONG

Action figure, Toho's Kong, plastic, 7.5 in., Bandai,
   Japanese import, 1993 (Figure 1-37) 25-35

KING SEESAR · KING CAESAR

Action figure, King Seesar (Caesar), plastic, 8 in.,
   1993 (Figure 1-38) 20-30

Glow-in-the-dark miniature figure, King Seesar, light
   orange plastic, 1.5 in., Bandai, 1993 5-10

MECHAGODZILLA · SUPER MECHAGODZILLA

Action figure, MechaGodzilla, soft plastic, 4.5 in.,
   Bandai, Big Godzilla boxed series, 1994 . . . . . $10-20

Action figure, MechaGodzilla 1974, plastic, 8 in.,
   Bandai, 1983 (Figure 1-39) 100-150

Action figure, plastic, 9 in., Bandai 1994
   (Figure 1-40) 35-45

Glow-in-the-dark miniature figure, MechaGodzilla
   1974, yellow plastic, 1.5 in., Bandai, 1993 5-10

Miniature figure, MechaGodzilla 1974, silver plastic,
   1.5 in., Bandai, 1993 5-9

Miniature figure, MechaGodzilla 1988, silver plastic,
   1.5 in., Bandai, 1993 (Figure 1-41) 5-9

"Super-real" painted miniature figure, Super
   MechaGodzilla, 2.5 in., Bandai, 1995
   (Figure 1-42) 6-12

MECHANIKONG

Action figure, Toho's MechaniKong, plastic, 7.5 in.,
   Japanese import, Bandai, 1991 (Figure 1-43) . . 95-125

(Figure 1-36) Hedorah, Bandai.

(Figure 1-35) Glow-in-the-dark Hedorah, Bandai.

(Figure 1-33) Godzillasaurus, Bandai.

(Figure 1-34) Miniature Gorosaurus, Bandai.

(Figure 1-37) Toho's Kong, Bandai.

(Figure 1-38) King Seesar, Bandai.

(Figure 1-39) MechaGodzilla 1974, Bandai.

(Figure 1-40) MechaGodzilla, Bandai.

(Figure 1-41) Miniature Mecha-Godzilla 1988, Bandai.

(Figure 1-42) "Super-real" miniature Super Mecha-Godzilla, Bandai.

MEGALON

Action figure, Megalon, plastic, 9 in., Bandai, 1991 (Figure 1-44) $110-140

Action figure, Megalon, Bullmark reissue, Bandai, 1992 35-50

Glow-in-the-dark miniature figure, Megalon, light orange plastic, 1.5 in., Bandai, 1993 5-10

MINYA · BABY GODZILLA · LITTLE GODZILLA · GODZILLA JR.

Action figure, Baby Godzilla, 6 in., Bandai, Godzilla Forever series, 1996 (Figure 1-45) $15-25

Action figure, Godzilla Jr., from *Godzilla vs. Destroyah*, Bandai, 1995 (Figure 1-46) 20-30

Action figure, Little Godzilla, 7-10 in., Bandai . . . 85-110

Action figure, Little Godzilla, 3.75 in. with stand, Bandai, Big Godzilla boxed series, 1994 (Figure 1-47) 10-20

Action figure, Minya, Bullmark reissue, Bandai, 1992 35-50

Glow-in-the-dark miniature figure, Godzilla Jr., light orange plastic, 1.5 in., Bandai, 1993 (Figure 1-48) 5-10

Miniature figure, Baby Godzilla, detailed gray vinyl, 1.5 in., marked "T.T.," Bandai, 1994 (Figure 1-49) 5-9

Miniature figure, Baby Godzilla, silver plastic, 1.5 in., Bandai, 1993 (Figure 1-50) 5-9

Miniature figure, Baby Godzilla, reddish-pink plastic, 1.5 in., Bandai, 1995 5-9

MOGUERA (MOGERA, M.O.G.U.E.R.A.)

Action figure, G-Force Moguera, soft plastic, 4.5 in., Bandai, Big Godzilla boxed series, 1994 10-20

Action figure, Moguera, old style, 7.5 in., Bandai 1994 (Figure 1-51) 35-50

Action figure, Moguera, with darker blue, plastic, 8.5 in., Bandai, 1994 (Figure 1-52) 25-40

Miniature figure, Moguera, detailed gray vinyl, 1.5 in., marked "T.T.," Bandai, 1994 5-9

(Figure 1-47) Little Godzilla, 3.75 in., Bandai.

(Figure 1-48) Glow-in-the-dark Godzilla Jr., Bandai.

(Figure 1-43) Toho's MechaniKong, Bandai.

(Figure 1-45) Baby Godzilla, 6 in., Godzilla Forever series, Bandai.

(Figure 1-46) Godzilla Jr., from Godzilla vs. Destroyah, *Bandai.*

(Figure 1-44) Megalon, Bandai.

36

(Figure 1-49) Miniature Baby Godzilla, detailed gray vinyl, Bandai.

(Figure 1-50) Miniature Baby Godzilla, silver plastic, Bandai.

(Figure 1-52) Moguera, 8.5 in., with darker blue, Bandai.

(Figure 1-51) Moguera, 7.5 in., Bandai.

(Figure 1-56) Mothra Larva, 7 in., Bandai.

Miniature figure, Moguera, reddish-pink plastic, 1.5 in., Bandai, 1995 . . . . $5-9

MOTHRA

Action figure, Classic Mothra, Bandai, 15 x 8.25-in. blue box, 1996 (Figure 1-53) 30-40

Action figure, Classic Mothra, fuzzy pink body, Bandai, 15 x 8.25-in. green box, 1992 (Figure 1-54) 40-50

Action figure, Mothra 1992, adult form, standard size, Bandai 50-75

Action figure, Mothra, Bandai, 12.5 x 7.25-in. green box, 1996-1997 (Figure 1-55) $25-35

Action figure, Mothra, Bullmark reissue, Bandai, 1992 35-50

Action figure, Mothra Larva, 7 in. long, Bandai, 1991 (Figure 1-56) 100-150

Action figure, Mothra Larva, cream-colored plastic, blue eyes, 7.5 in. long, Bandai, 1996 (Figure 1-57) 8-12

Miniature figure, Mothra, light blue vinyl, 1.5 in., Bandai, 1996 4-8

Miniature figure, Mothra Larva, detailed gray vinyl,
1.5 in., marked "T.T.," Bandai, 1994 . . . . $5-9

RODAN

Action figure, Fire Rodan, 7 in., Bandai, 1993
(Figure 1-58) 25-45

Action figure, Rodan 1956, plastic, 7.5 in., Bandai,
1991 (Figure 1-59) 100-135

Action figure, Rodan, 6 in. tall, Bandai, Godzilla
Forever series, 1996 (Figure 1-60) 40-60

Action figure, Rodan, Bullmark reissue, Bandai,
1992 35-50

Miniature figure, modern Rodan, light blue vinyl,
1.5 in., Bandai, 1996 . . . . $4-8

Miniature figure, modern Rodan, reddish-pink plastic,
1.5 in., Bandai, 1993 (Figure 1-61) 5-9

(Figure 1-57) Mothra Larva, 7.5 in., 1996, Bandai.

*(Figure 1-60) Rodan,
Godzilla Forever series,
Bandai.*

*(Figure 1-61) Miniature
Rodan, reddish-pink plas-
tic, Bandai.*

(Figure 1-55) Mothra, Bandai.

(Figure 1-54) Classic Mothra, fuzzy pink body, Bandai.

(Figure 1-53) Classic Mothra, Bandai.

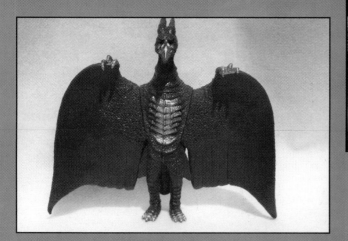

(Figure 1-59) Rodan 1956, Bandai.

(Figure 1-58) Fire Rodan, Bandai.

SPACE GODZILLA

Action figure, Space Godzilla, plastic, 10 in.,
Bandai, 1994 (Figure 1-62) $35-60

Action figure, Space Godzilla, soft plastic, Bandai,
Big Godzilla boxed series, 1994 (Figure 1-63) . . 10-20

Miniature figure, Space Godzilla, detailed gray vinyl,
1.5 in., marked "T.T.," Bandai, 1994
(Figure 1-64) 5-9

"Super-real" painted miniature figure, Space
Godzilla, 2.5 in., Bandai, 1995 (Figure 1-65) 6-12

Translucent Superdeformed Space Godzilla, from
machines in Japanese theater lobbies, 1.5 in.,
Bandai, 1995 2-5

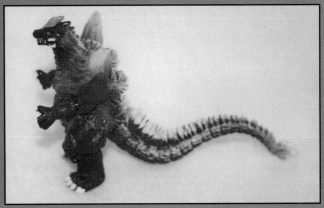

*(Figure 1-65) "Super-real" miniature Space
Godzilla, Bandai.*

(Figure 1-62) Space Godzilla, Bandai.

*(Figure 1-63) Space
Godzilla, Big Godzilla
boxed series, Bandai.*

*(Figure 1-64) Miniature
Space Godzilla, 1.5 in.,
Bandai.*

MULTI-MONSTER PLAYSETS

Battle Set, Godzilla vs. Destroyer, with five
    monsters, Bandai, 1995 . . . . $40-65

Battle Set, Godzilla vs. MechaGodzilla, with three
    2-in. figures, plastic, Bandai, 1993
    (Figure 1-66) 20-30

Diorama Playset, each half is boxed separately with
    four figures, Bandai, 1993, each half 25-35

Monster Island Playset, eight small scale Bandai
    figures, boxed, 1990s (Figure 1-67) 140-165

Superdeformed boxed set, Godzilla and nine friends,
    hollow plastic, Bandai, 1992 (Figure 1-68) 20-40

OTHERS

Great Hydra of Yamato, plastic figure, 13 in.,
    Bandai, 1994 (Figure 1-69) 120-140

Jiras (Godzilla with frill added to neck for
    Ultraman series), light blue vinyl, 2 in., Bandai,
    1996 (Figure 1-70) 4-8

(Figure 1-67) Monster Island Playset, Bandai.

*(Figure 1-68) Boxed set,
Superdeformed monsters,
Bandai.*

*(Figure 1-70) Jiras,
Bandai.*

(Figure 1-66) Battle Set, Bandai.

(Figure 1-69) Great Hydra of Yamato, Bandai.

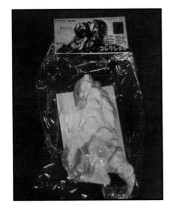

(Figure 1-71) Hedorah,
5 in., Bare Model.

(Figure 1-72) Gabera,
10 in., Bullmark.

(Figure 1-73) Ghidrah, 10.25 in., Bullmark.

BARE MODEL

HEDORAH · SMOG MONSTER

Action figure, Hedorah, yellow painted plastic, 5 in.,
in poly bag with topper, 1997 (Figure 1-71). . . $35-55

MULTI-MONSTER PLAYSETS

Yog! Monster From Space, four monsters, 4 in., Bare
Model, 1997, set 60-80

BULLMARK

ANGILAS · ANGUIRUS · ANGURUS

Action figure, Angilas, stands upright, orange
painted vinyl, Bullmark, 1970 200-350

Action figure, Angilas, green vinyl, standing upright
with arms out, small, Bullmark, 1971 50-100

BARAGON

Action figure, Baragon, orange painted vinyl, 9 in.,
(from Marusan mold), Bullmark, 1970 200-250

Action figure, Baragon, large size, holding red
tower, Bullmark, 1971 . . . . $500-800

EBIRAH

Action figure, Ebirah, orange painted vinyl (no paint
on feelers), Bullmark (no mark), 1970 200-400

GABERA

Action figure, Gabera, green painted vinyl, 10 in.,
Marusan mark on foot, Bullmark, 1969
(Figure 1-72) 150-250

Action figure, Gabera, green painted vinyl, 10 in.,
Bullmark mark on foot, Bullmark, 1970 200-300

GHIDRAH · GHIDORAH · KING GHIDORAH

Action figure, Ghidrah, orange painted vinyl,
10.25 in., Bullmark, 1970 (Figure 1-73) 175-350

Action figure, Ghidrah, vinyl, small with green
wings, 5.5 in., Bullmark, 1975 125-250

Action figure, Ghidrah, orange painted vinyl, giant
size with open mouths, Bullmark, 1970 . . . . $500-800

GIGAN

Action figure, Gigan, blue and red painted vinyl,
9 in., Bullmark, 1972 150-350

Action figure, Gigan, green and red painted vinyl,
9 in., Bullmark, 1973 250-500

Action figure, Gigan, small size, Bullmark,
1972 100-200

GODZILLA

Action figure, Godzilla, vinyl, made from
Marusan mold, Bullmark, 1970s 300-400

Action figure, Godzilla, blue or brown vinyl,
small scale, Bullmark, 1975 50-100

Action figure, Godzilla, large size, holds red
tower, Bullmark, 1970, rare 750-1000

Action figure, Sparking Godzilla, Bullmark,
1972 300-600

GOROSAURUS

Action figure, Gorosaurus, blue painted vinyl,
8.75 in., Bullmark, 1970 (Figure 1-74) $200-350

HEDORAH · SMOG MONSTER

Action figure, Hedorah, yellow painted vinyl,
10 in., Bullmark, 1971 300-500

Action figure, Hedorah, pink painted vinyl,
10 in., Bullmark, 1971, rare version 1,000-1,500

Action figure, Hedorah, small version, yellow
painted vinyl, Bullmark, 1971 200-300

JET-JAGUAR

Action figure, Jet-Jaguar, large size, vinyl,
Bullmark, 1973, rare 1,000-1,500

Action figure, Jet-Jaguar, small size, vinyl,
Bullmark, 1973 150-300

(Figure 1-74) Gorosaurus, Bullmark.

(Figure 1-75) Missile-Firing MechaGodzilla, Bullmark.

MECHAGODZILLA

Action figure, MechaGodzilla, vinyl, small, gray
and black, Bullmark, 1975 . . . . $100-175

Action figure, Missile-Firing MechaGodzilla, vinyl,
9.75 in., Bullmark, boxed, 1974
(Figure 1-75) 500-800

MECHANIKONG

Action figure, MechaniKong, blue painted vinyl,
10 in., Bullmark, 1970 (Figure 1-76) 200-350

MEGALON

Action figure, Megalon, painted vinyl,
Bullmark, 1973 1,600-2,000

Action figure, Megalon, small size, painted
vinyl, Bullmark, 1973 300-500

MINYA

Action figure, Minya, larger than Marusan figures,
red vinyl, Bullmark, 1969 150-250

(Figure 1-76) MechaniKong, Bullmark.

MOGUERA

Action figure, Moguera, painted vinyl, (two color
variations), Bullmark, 1970 . . . . $200-350

MOTHRA

Action figure, Mothra Adult, painted vinyl,
Bullmark, 1970 350-450

Action figure, Mothra Larva , painted yellow
vinyl, Bullmark, 1975 175-250

RODAN

Action figure, Rodan, blue and orange painted
vinyl, 10 in., Bullmark, 1970 300-400

Action figure, Rodan, pink vinyl, small size,
Bullmark, 1971 100-250

SMOG MONSTER (SEE HEDORAH)

TITANOSAURUS

Action figure, Titanosaurus, green painted vinyl,
Bullmark, 1975 200-400

VARAN THE UNBELIEVABLE

Action figure, Varan, orange painted vinyl,
Bullmark, 1970 200-350

IMPERIAL

GODZILLA

Action figure, Godzilla, green painted rubber, 5 in.,
with tag, Imperial 1984 (Figure 1-77) 6-10

*(Figure 1-77) Godzilla, 5
in., Imperial.*

*(Figure 1-78) Godzilla, 7
in., Imperial.*

(Figure 1-79) Godzilla, 15 in., Imperial.

(Figure 1-80) Battra Larva, Kaiyodo.

(Figure 1-81) Translucent Godzilla, G-Con exclusive, Marmit.

(Figure 1-83) Matango, M1.

Action figure, Godzilla, green painted rubber, 7 in.,
  on card, Imperial, 1984 (Figure 1-78) $12-20

Action figure, Godzilla, green painted rubber,
  15 in., 1984 (Figure 1-79) 15-25

KAIYODO

BATTRA

Figure, Battra Larva , plastic, 4.75 in. long,
  Kaiyodo, in poly bag, 1993 (Figure 1-80) 30-40

M1

MATANGO

(ATTACK OF THE MUSHROOM PEOPLE)

Vinyl figure, Matango, from
  Marusan/Bullmark mold 40-60

Vinyl figure, Matango, limited edition
  glow version 50-80

MARMIT

BARAGON

Action figure, Baragon, Vinyl Paradise series,
  in poly bag, Marmit, 1997 . . . . $35-70

GODZILLA

Godzilla 1954, Vinyl Paradise series, in poly bag,
  Marmit, 1997 35-70

Godzilla 1955, Vinyl Paradise series, in poly bag,
  Marmit, 1997 35-70

Godzilla 1962, Vinyl Paradise series, in poly bag,
  Marmit, 1997 35-70

Godzilla 1964, Vinyl Paradise series, in poly bag,
  Marmit, 1997 35-70

Translucent green figure, 10.75 in., G-Con exclusive,
  only 300 made, Marmit, 1996-1997
  (Figure 1-81) 60-100

MANDA

Action figure, Manda, green painted plastic,
17.5 in. long, 1997 (Figure 1-82) $35-70

MATANGO
(ATTACK OF THE MUSHROOM PEOPLE)

Action figure, painted plastic, many color variations,
9 in., Vinyl Paradise series, 1997 (Figure 1-83). . 35-70

MOGUERA

Action figure, Moguera, 10 in., Vinyl Paradise series,
1998 35-70

(Figure 1-82) Manda, Marmit.

(Figure 1-84) Rodan, Vinyl Paradise series, Marmit.

RODAN

Action figure, Rodan, 9.5 in., Vinyl Paradise series,
in poly bag, marked "Ages 18 and up"
(Figure 1-84) $35-70

VARAN THE UNBELIEVABLE

Action figure, Varan, 10 in., Vinyl Paradise series,
Marmit, 1998 35-70

MARUSAN
(THE FIRST COMPANY TO PRODUCE GODZILLA ACTION FIGURES!)

BARAGON

Action figure, Baragon, orange painted vinyl,
Marusan, 1966 400-450

EBIRAH

Action figure, Ebirah, red painted vinyl,
(paint on feelers) Marusan, 1966 350-500

GIANT GORILLA · KING KONG

Action figure, blue painted vinyl, Marusan,
1967, rare 1500-2000

Figure, Giant Gorilla, pink or blue vinyl, 8.75 in.,
Marusan Creative, poly bag with topper, 1997
(Figures 1-85, 1-86) 30-50

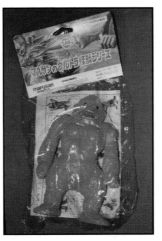 

(Figure 1-85) Giant
Gorilla, pink, Marusan.

(Figure 1-86) Giant
Gorilla, blue, Marusan.

GODZILLA

Action figure, the very first Godzilla figure
   produced, green vinyl, Marusan, 1966 . . . . . $500-750

Action figure, Godzilla, blue vinyl, Marusan,
   1966 400-600

GOROSAURUS

Action figure, Gorosaurus, blue vinyl, Marusan,
   1967 250-400

Action figure, Gorosaurus, blue vinyl with white
   stomach, Marusan, 1967 400-600

MECHANIKONG

Action figure, MehcaniKong, painted vinyl,
   Marusan, 1967 350-500

MINYA

Action figure, Minya, red vinyl, (smaller than
   Bullmark Minya), Marusan, 1967 500-800

Action figure, Minya, green vinyl, (smaller than
   Bullmark Minya), Marusan, 1967 400-700

MOTHRA

Action figure, Mothra Adult, (two color
   variations), vinyl, Marusan 300-500

MATTEL
GODZILLA

Godzilla's Gang, featuring Godzilla figure with
   seven Ultra monster figures, Mattel, 1978 . . . 250-400

Godzilla figure only, marked "Made in Taiwan,"
   Mattel, 1978 50-100

POPY
BARAGON

Action figure, Baragon, Popy, 1978 100-200

GHIDRAH · GHIDORAH · KING GHIDORAH

Action figure, King Ghidorah, Popy, 1978 100-200

GIGAN

Action figure, Gigan, Popy, 1978 150-250

GODZILLA

Action figure, Godzilla, small size, Popy, 1979 . . . $50-75

Action figure, Godzilla, medium-size, Popy,
   late 1970s 50-150

Action figure, Godzilla, large size, Popy,
   1979 150-250

Action figure, Godzilla, giant size with red paint,
   Popy, 1979 200-400

MECHAGODZILLA

Action figure, MechaGodzilla, Popy, 1979 100-200

MOTHRA

Action figure, Mothra Larva, tiny red eyes, 14 in.
   long, Popy/Bandai, 1984 (Figure 1-87) 250-350

RODAN

Action figure, Rodan, Popy, 1978 100-200

TAKARA
MOTHRA

Superdeformed Mothra figure, plastic, gold top,
   blue eyes, 4.25 in. long, Takara, 1997
   (Figure 1-88) 12-20

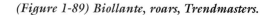

(Figure 1-89) Biollante, roars, Trendmasters.

(Figure 1-87) Mothra Larva, Popy/Bandai.

(Figure 1-88) Superdeformed Mothra, Takara.

TRENDMASTERS

Note: Trendmasters items were originally produced in 1994, with "Godzilla, King of the Monsters" packaging. The following year, 1995, the company introduced the "Godzilla Wars" series.

BATTRA

Action figure, Battra Adult, 6 in., Trendmasters, Godzilla Wars series, 1995 . . . . $6-12

BIOLLANTE

Action figure, Biollante, roars, Trendmasters, King of the Monsters series, 1994 (Figure 1-89) 20-30

GHIDRAH · GHIDORAH · KING GHIDORAH · MECHAGHIDORAH

Action figure, Ghidorah, 6 in., Trendmasters, first series, 1994 5-10

Action figure, King Ghidorah, 6 in., roars, Godzilla Wars series, 1995 5-10

Action figure, MechaGhidorah, 6 in., first series, 1994 5-10

(Figure 1-91) Gigan, roars, Trendmasters.

Action figure, Mecha King Ghidorah, roars, 6 in., Godzilla Wars series, 1995 (Figure 1-90) $5-10

GIGAN

Action figure, Gigan, roars, 6 in., with trading card, Trendmasters, 1994 (Figure 1-91) 5-10

GODZILLA

Action figure, Godzilla, black plastic, 4 in., 1994 2-4

Action figure, Godzilla, 6 in., original series, 1994 (Figure 1-92) 4-9

Action figure, Godzilla, roars, 10 in., original series, 1994 (Figure 1-93). 6-12

Action figure, Godzilla, roars, with trading card, Godzilla Wars series, 1995 6-12

Action figure, Supercharged Godzilla, roars, Godzilla Wars series, 1995 (Figure 1-94) 6-12

Action Playset, with roaring 4 in. Godzilla, combat vehicles, and men, 1995 (Figure 1-95) . . 6-12

Power-Up Godzilla with Snap-On Armor, Godzilla Wars series, boxed (Figure 1-96) 15-20

Resin Prototype, Cyclatic Walker Godzilla (not produced), 7.5 in., est. 10 produced, 1995 (Figure 1-97). 200-300

(Figure 1-94) Supercharged Godzilla, Trendmasters.

Figure 1-90) Mecha King Ghidorah, Trendmasters.

(Figure 1-98) Garuda warship, Trendmasters.

(Figure 1-92) Godzilla, 6 in., Trendmasters.

(Figure 1-96) Power-Up Godzilla, Trendmasters.

(Figure 1-97) Resin prototype, Trendmasters.

(Figure 1-93) Godzilla, 10 in., roars, Trendmasters.

(Figure 1-95) Action Playset, Trendmasters.

HUMAN FIGURES

MECHAGODZILLA · SUPER MECHAGODZILLA

MOGUERA · M.O.G.U.E.R.A.

(Figure 1-99) Moguera, Godzilla Wars series, Trendmasters.

MOTHRA

Action figure, Mothra, roars, 6 in., Trendmasters, original series, 1994 (Figure 1-100) $5-10

Action figure, Mothra, roars, 6 in., Trendmasters, Godzilla Wars series, 1995 5-10

Action playset, Mothra, tanks, and soldiers, Trendmasters, 1994 (Figure 1-101) 6-12

RODAN

Action figure, Rodan, 4 in., Trendmasters, original series, carded, 1994 (Figure 1-102) $2-4

Action figure, Rodan, roars, 6 in., Trendmasters, original series, boxed, 1994 (Figure 1-103) 6-12

Action figure, Rodan, roars, 6 in., Trendmasters, Godzilla Wars series, 1995 5-10

Power-Up Cyber Rodan, with snap-on armor, Godzilla Wars series, boxed (Figure 1-104) 15-20

SPACE GODZILLA

Action figure, Space Godzilla, roars, 6 in., Trendmasters, Godzilla Wars series, 1995 (Figure 1-105) 5-10

Action figure, Space Godzilla, roars, 10 in., Trendmasters, Godzilla Wars series, 1995 (Figure 1-106) 6-12

(Figure 1-100) Mothra, roars, Trendmasters.

(Figure 1-101) Action Playset, Mothra, fights tanks and soldiers, Trendmasters.

(Figure 1-104) Power-Up Cyber Rodan, Trendmasters.

(Figure 1-102) Rodan, 4 in., Trendmasters.

(Figure 1-103) Rodan, 6 in., Trendmasters.

(Figure 1-106) Space Godzilla by Trendmasters (left)
and Bandai.

(Figure 1-105) Space Godzilla, Godzilla Wars series,
Trendmasters.

(Figure 1-107) 40th Anniversary Collector's Set,
Trendmasters.

MULTI-MONSTER PLAYSETS

40th Anniversary Collectors set of nine 4-in. figures,
Trendmasters, 1994 (Figure 1-107) $30-40

Two-pack, Godzilla vs. Ghidorah, carded,
Trendmasters, 1994 (Figure 1-108) 4-7

Two-pack, Godzilla and Battra in mismarked
Godzilla vs. MechaGhidorah package,
Trendmasters, 1994 (Figure 1-109) 5-10

Two-pack, Godzilla vs. Mothra (adult), carded,
Trendmasters, 1994 (Figure 1-110) 4-7

YAMAKATSU

ANGILAS · ANGUIRUS · ANGURUS

Figure, Angilas, black plastic, yellow highlights,
9.5 in., Yamakatsu, 1983 (Figure 1-111) $45-85

BARAGON

Figure, Baragon, Yamakatsu, 1983 85-110

GHIDRAH · GHIDORAH · KING GHIDORAH

Action figure, King Ghidorah, 7 in., Yamakatsu,
1983 130-160

GODZILLA

Action figure, Godzilla, with silver fins, 6.5 in.,
Yamakatsu, 1983 (Figure 1-112) 35-70

Action figure, Godzilla, with gold fins, 6.5 in.,
Yamakatsu, 1983 (Figure 1-113) 40-75

Action figure, Godzilla, smaller version with
silver fins, Yamakatsu, 1983 12-20

Action figure, Godzilla, smaller version with
gold fins, Yamakatsu, 1983 12-20

MECHAGODZILLA

Action figure, MechaGodzilla, 6.5 in., Yamakatsu,
1983 70-90

MECHANIKONG

Action figure, MechaniKong, silver plastic, 6.5 in.,
Yamakatsu, 1983 (Figure 1-114) 40-75

(Figure 1-108) Godzilla vs. Ghidorah, Trendmasters.

*(Figure 1-109) Godzilla and Battra in mismarked
package, Trendmasters.*

(Figure 1-112) Godzilla, with silver fins, Yamakatsu.

(Figure 1-110) Godzilla vs. Mothra, Trendmasters.

(Figure 1-113) Godzilla, with gold fins, Yamakatsu.

(Figure 1-111) Angilas, 9.5 in., Yamakatsu.

MOTHRA

Action figure, Mothra Larva, silver, with pink eyes,
7.5 in., Yamakatsu, 1983 (Figure 1-115) $25-55

YUTAKA

GODZILLA

Superdeformed Godzilla, hollow gray and silver
plastic, 1.5 in., Yutaka (Figure 1-116) 8-12

MECHAGODZILLA

Action figure, MechaGodzilla, small size, Yutaka . . 10-15

MOGUERA

Action figure, Moguera, 4 in., Yutaka, 1994
(Figure 1-117) 8-12

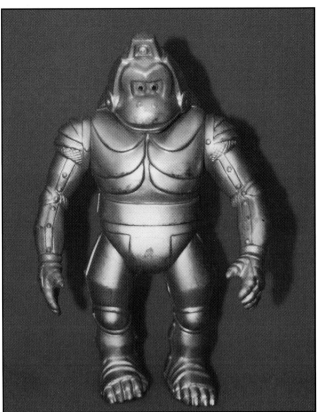

(Figure 1-114) MechaniKong, 6.5 in., Yamakatsu.

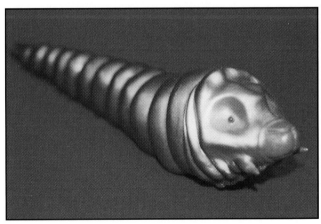

(Figure 1-115) Mothra Larva, 7.5 in., Yamakatsu.

MULTI-MONSTER PLAYSETS

Action figures set, larger MechaGodzilla and
seven small, colorful friends, Yutaka, 1993
(Figure 1-118) $25-45

Battle set; Godzilla, Ghidrah, Mothra, Battra and
MechaGodzilla; Yutaka 25-50

Ghidrah Battle set, Godzilla and Ghidrah, boxed,
Yutaka 25-50

Superdeformed boxed set, Part 2, four figures,
Yutaka, 1990s (Figure 1-119) 20-35

(Figure 1-117) Moguera, Yutaka.

(Figure 1-116) Superdeformed Godzilla, 1.5 in., Yutaka.

(Figure 1-119) Superdeformed figures boxed set, Yutaka.

(Figure 1-118) Action figures set featuring MechaGodzilla and seven other monsters, Yutaka.

UNLICENSED, UNKNOWN, NO MARK

GODZILLA

Action figure, poseable, green and silver plastic,
6 in., no mark (Figure 1-120) $30-60

Action figure, unlicensed with incorrect spines,
blue vinyl, 9 in., China (Figure 1-121) 6-8

Action figure, unlicensed, gray plastic, articulate,
13.5 in., Dor Nei, 1986 China (Figure 1-122) . . 10-15

Action figure, unlicensed, hard plastic, 14 in., black
and orange, made in China (Figure 1-123) $12-20

Superdeformed Godzilla 2 in., hollow plastic, green
with silver paint (Figure 1-124) 3-5

OTHERS

Superdeformed Baragon, 2 in., hollow plastic, yellow
with silver paint (Figure 1-125) 3-5

Superdeformed Ghidrah, 2 in., hollow plastic, yellow
with black eyes 2-4

(Figure 1-120) Godzilla action figure, unmarked.

(Figure 1-121) Godzilla action figure, with incorrect spines.

(Figure 1-222) Godzilla action figure, gray plastic.

(Figure 1-123) Godzilla action figure, black and orange plastic.

(Figure 1-124) Superdeformed Godzilla.

(Figure 1-125) Superdeformed Baragon.

CHAPTER TWO
MOVIE POSTERS
FILM, VIDEO, & THEATER MATERIAL

ATRAGON

Lobby card, Manda pictured on *Atragon*
  lobby card, 1965 . . . . $25-35
Movie poster, *Atragon*, original Japanese one-sheet,
  1963 (Figure 2-1). 85-150
Movie poster, *Atragon*, one-sheet, U.S.,
  1965 (Figure 2-2) 35-50

DESTROY ALL MONSTERS

8 mm film, *Destroy All Monsters*, Ken films, 5.5-in.
  box, 1969 30-40
Lobby card, *Destroy All Monsters*, U.S., 1968,
  (scene dependent) 15-30
Movie poster, *Destroy All Monsters*, one-sheet,
  Japanese, 1968 (Figure 2-3) 225-275
Movie poster, *Destroy All Monsters*, one-sheet,
  U.S., 1969 (Figure 2-4) 100-150
Video, *Destroy All Monsters*, ADV, U.S. version,
  1998 (Figure 2-5). 15-20

(Figure 2-1) Movie poster, Atragon, Japanese.

(Figure 2-2) Movie poster,
Atragon, *U.S.*

(Figure 2-4) Movie poster,
Destroy All Monsters, *U.S.*

(Figure 2-3) Movie poster, **Destroy All Monsters,** *Japanese.*

(Figure 2-5) Video, **Destroy All Monsters.**

(Figure 2-6) Laserdisc, Ghidrah the Three-Headed Monster, *Japanese.*

(Figures 2-7—2-13) Lobby cards, Ghidrah the Three-Headed Monster.

Video poster, *Destroy All Monsters,* U.S.,
36 x 24 in., 1998 . . . . $8-12

GHIDRAH THE THREE-HEADED MONSTER

Laserdisc, *Ghidrah, the Three-Headed Monster,*
Toho (Figure 2-6) 50-60
Lobby card, *Ghidrah the Three-Headed Monster,*
U.S., 1964, (scene dependent)
(Figures 2-7—2-13) 10-50
Program, *Ghidrah the Three-Headed Monster,*
1964 100-200

Movie poster, *Ghidrah the Three-Headed Monster,*
one-sheet, Japanese, 1964 (Figure 2-14) . . . $600-800
Movie poster, *Ghidrah the Three-Headed Monster,*
one-sheet, U.S., 1965 (Figure 2-15) 150-200
Movie poster, *Ghidrah the Three-Headed Monster*
Japanese, 1971 re-release 80-125
Super 8 mm film, *Ghidrah the Three-Headed
Monster,* boxed, 1960s 30-40
Video, *Monster of Monsters, Ghidorah,* Japanese,
blue border on box, Toho, 1964
(Figure 2-16) 60-75

(Figure 2-17) Movie poster, Godzilla's Counterattack.

(Figure 2-15) Movie poster, Ghidrah the Three-Headed Monster, U.S.

(Figure 2-14) Movie poster, Ghidrah the Three-Headed Monster, Japanese.

(Figure 2-16) Video, Monster of Monsters.

GIGANTIS THE FIRE MONSTER (GODZILLA'S COUNTERATTACK)

Lobby card, *Gigantis the Fire Monster*
  (with Angilas), U.S. version, 1959 . . . . $40-60
Movie poster, *Godzilla's Counterattack,*
  original Japanese one-sheet, 1955
  (Figure 2-17) 2,000-3,000
Movie poster, *Gigantis the Fire Monster*, advance
  one-sheet, U.S., red and black, 1959
  (Figure 2-18) 100-150
Movie poster, *Gigantis the Fire Monster*, one-sheet,
  U.S., shows two monsters fighting, 1959 75-125
Video, *Godzilla Raids Again*, Japanese, blue border
  on box, Toho, 1955 (Figure 2-19) 60-75

GODZILLA/GOJIRA (1954, JAPAN)
GODZILLA, KING OF THE MONSTERS (1956, U.S.)

Lobby card, *Godzilla King of the Monsters*,
  U.S. version (scene dependent) 50-250
Movie poster, *Godzilla*, one-sheet, Japanese
  version, 1954 (Figure 2-20) 4,000-6,000
Movie poster, *Godzilla*, half-sheet or insert,
  Japanese version, 1954 1,500-3,000

(Figure 2-18) Movie poster, **Gigantis the Fire Monster.**

(Figure 2-19) Video, **Godzilla Raids Again.**

(Figure 2-21) Movie poster, **Godzilla, King of the Monsters,** *U.S.*

Movie poster, half-sheet or a "speed poster"
    insert, Japanese version of U.S. version
    (Figure 2-23) $1,200-2,000
Movie poster, *Godzilla,* Japanese reproduction . . . 75-125
Video, *Gojira,* original Japanese film without
    Raymond Burr, blue border on box, Toho,
    1954 (Figure 2-24) 60-75
Video, *Godzilla, King of the Monsters,* U.S. version,
    Simitar, 1998 (Figure 2-25). 15-20

GODZILLA 1984 (JAPAN)
GODZILLA 1985 (U.S.)

Movie poster, *Godzilla 1984,* Japanese,
    photo version 30-45
Movie poster, *Godzilla 1984,* Japanese,
    artwork version 75-125
Movie poster, *Godzilla 1985,* U.S. 20-30
Program, *Godzilla 1984,* 11.75 x 8.25 in., 1984
    (Figure 2-26) 15-25
Video, *Godzilla 1984,* Japanese, circle in upper
    corner of box, Toho, 1984 (Figure 2-27) 60-75

(Figure 2-20) Movie poster, **Godzilla,** *Japanese.*

Movie poster, *Godzilla, King of the Monsters,*
    one-sheet, U.S. version, 1956
    (Figure 2-21) $1,000-2,500
Movie poster, *Godzilla, King of the Monsters,*
    one-sheet, Japanese poster for U.S. version
    (Figure 2-22) 2,000-3,000
Movie poster, *Godzilla, King of the Monsters,*
    half-sheet or insert, U.S. version 1,000-1,500

(Figure 2-22) Movie poster, Godzilla, King of the Monsters, *Japanese.*

(Figure 2-23) Movie poster, Godzilla King of the Monsters, *"speed poster" insert.*

(Figure 2-26) Program, Godzilla 1984.

(Figure 2-27) Video, Godzilla 1984.

(Figure 2-25) Video, Godzilla King of the Monsters.

(Figure 2-24) Video, Gojira.

GODZILLA POWER HOUR (TV)

Animation cel, *The Godzilla Power Hour*,
Filmation, 1970s $200-350
Production drawing, Filmation, 1970s 75-125

GODZILLA VS. BIOLLANTE

Laserdisc, *Godzilla vs. Biollante*, Toho 50-60
Movie poster, *Godzilla vs. Biollante*, Japanese, 1989
(high end for artwork style) 40-100
Video, *Godzilla vs. Biollante*, Japanese, circle in
upper corner of box, Toho, 1989
(Figure 2-28) 70-85

GODZILLA VS. DESTROYAH

Movie poster, *Godzilla vs. Destroyah*, Japanese,
photo version, 1995 (Figure 2-29) 20-30

Movie poster, *Godzilla vs. Destroyah*, Japanese,
painted version, 1995 . . . . $20-30
Program, *Godzilla vs. Destroyah*, 11.75 x 8.25 in.,
1995 (Figure 2-30) 15-25
Video, *Godzilla vs. Destroyah*, Japanese, circle in
upper corner of box, Toho, 1995 (Figure 2-31) . 70-85

GODZILLA VS. GIGAN (GODZILLA ON MONSTER ISLAND)

Movie poster, *Godzilla vs. Gigan*, one-sheet,
Japanese, 1972 (Figure 2-32) 75-125
Movie poster, *Godzilla on Monster Island*,
one-sheet, U.S., 1973 50-80

GODZILLA VS. KING GHIDORAH

Movie poster, *Godzilla vs. King Ghidorah*, Japanese,
1991, (high end for artwork style) 25-75

(Figure 2-28) Video, Godzilla vs. Biollante.

(Figure 2-29) Movie poster,
Godzilla vs. Destroyah.

(Figure 2-30) Program,
Godzilla vs. Destroyah.

(Figure 2-31) Video,
Godzilla vs. Destroyah.

(Figure 2-32) Movie poster,
Godzilla vs. Gigan.

(Figure 2-34) Video,
Godzilla vs. King
Ghidorah.

(Figure 2-36) Video,
Godzilla vs.
MechaGodzilla, 1974.

(Figure 2-33) Program, Godzilla vs. King Ghidorah.

Program, *Godzilla vs. King Ghidorah*,
    11.75 x 8.25 in., 1991 (Figure 2-33) $15-25
Video, *Godzilla vs. King Ghidorah*, Japanese,
    circle in upper corner of box, Toho, 1991
    (Figure 2-34) 70-85

GODZILLA VS. MECHAGODZILLA (1974)
GODZILLA VS. THE COSMIC (BIONIC) MONSTER

Movie poster, *Godzilla vs. MechaGodzilla*, Japanese,
    1974 (Figure 2-35) 75-125
Movie poster, *Godzilla vs. the Cosmic Monster*,
    U.S., 1975 60-90
Video, *Godzilla vs. MechaGodzilla*, Japanese, blue
    border on box, Toho, 1974 (Figure 2-36) 60-75

GODZILLA VS. MECHAGODZILLA (1993)

Movie poster, *Godzilla vs. MechaGodzilla*, Japanese,
    photo version, 1993 25-35
Movie poster, *Godzilla vs. MechaGodzilla*, Japanese,
    painted version, 1993 40-75

(Figure 2-35) Movie poster, Godzilla vs.
MechaGodzilla, 1974.

Video, *Godzilla vs. MechaGodzilla*, Japanese,
    circle in upper corner of box, Toho, 1993
    (Figure 2-37) $70-85

GODZILLA VS. MEGALON

Movie poster, *Godzilla vs. Megalon*, Japanese,
    1973 (Figure 2-38) 75-125

(Figure 2-39) Movie poster, Godzilla vs. Megalon, *U.S.*

(Figure 2-37) Video, Godzilla vs. Mecha-Godzilla, *1993.*

Movie poster, *Godzilla vs. Megalon,* one-sheet with
both on building tops, U.S., 1974
(Figure 2-39) $60-90
Video, American version 8-15

GODZILLA VS. MOTHRA (1992)

Laserdisc, *Godzilla vs. Mothra,* (dark cover
with Battra) Toho, 1992 (Figure 2-40) 50-60
Movie poster, *Godzilla vs. Mothra,* Japanese
(high end for artwork style), 1992 30-90
Program, *Godzilla vs. Mothra,* 11.75 x 8.25 in.,
1992 (Figure 2-41). 15-25
Video, *Godzilla vs. Mothra,* Japanese, circle in
upper corner of box, Toho, 1992 (Figure 2-42) . 70-85

GODZILLA VS. THE SEA MONSTER
EBIRAH, HORROR OF THE DEEP

Movie poster, *Godzilla vs. the Sea Monster,*
one-sheet, Japanese, 1966 (Figure 2-43) 250-350
Movie poster, *Godzilla vs. the Sea Monster,*
"speed poster," Japanese, 10 x 28.5 in., 1966
(Figure 2-44). 100-200

GODZILLA VS. THE SMOG MONSTER (GODZILLA
VS. HEDORAH)

Movie poster, *Godzilla vs. the Smog Monster,*
one-sheet, Japanese, 1971 (Figure 2-45) 100-165
Movie poster, *Godzilla vs. the Smog Monster,*
one-sheet, U.S., 1972 75-125
Video, *Godzilla vs. Hedorah,* Japanese, blue border
on box, Toho, 1971 (Figure 2-46) 60-75

(Figure 2-38) Movie poster, Godzilla vs.
Megalon, *Japanese.*

(Figure 2-40) Laserdisc, Godzilla vs. Mothra.

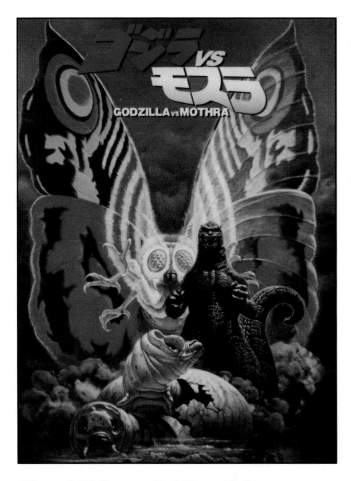

(Figure 2-41) Program, Godzilla vs. Mothra.

(Figure 2-42) Video, Godzilla vs. Mothra.

(Figure 2-43) Movie poster, Godzilla vs. the Sea Monster, *one-sheet.*

(Figure 2-44) Movie poster, Godzilla vs. the Sea Monster, *"speed poster."*

(Figure 2-45) Movie poster, Godzilla vs. the Smog Monster, *Japanese.*

(Figure 2-46) Video, Godzilla vs. Hedorah.

(Figure 2-47) Program, Godzilla vs. Space Godzilla.

GODZILLA VS. SPACE GODZILLA

Movie poster, *Godzilla vs. Space Godzilla*, Japanese,
    photo version, 1994 . . . . $20-25
Movie poster, *Godzilla vs. Space Godzilla*, Japanese,
    painted version, 1994 25-35
Program, *Godzilla vs. Space Godzilla*,
    11.75 x 8.25 in., 1994 (Figure 2-47). 15-25
Video, *Godzilla vs. Space Godzilla*, Japanese, circle in
    upper corner of box, Toho, 1994 (Figure 2-48) . 70-85

GODZILLA VS. THE THING (MOTHRA)

8 mm home movie, *Godzilla vs. the Thing*,
    with subtitles, boxed 25-40
Laserdisc, *Godzilla Against Mothra*, radio tower
    on cover, Toho Laserdisc (Figure 2-49) 50-60
Lobby card, *Godzilla vs. the Thing*, (with Mothra),
    U.S., 1964, (scene dependent) (Figure 2-50) . . 30-55
Monster manual, *Godzilla Against Mothra*, dist.
    in theaters, Japanese, 1963 (Figure 2-51) 60-95
Movie poster, *Godzilla Against Mothra*, original
    Japanese one-sheet, 1963 (Figure 2-52) 300-400
Movie poster, *Godzilla Against Mothra*,
    "speed poster," Japanese, 10 x 28.5 in., 1964
    (Figure 2-53) 100-200

(Figure 2-48) Video, Godzilla vs. Space Godzilla.

(Figure 2-49) Laserdisc, Godzilla Against Mothra.

(Figure 2-51) Monster manual, Godzilla Against Mothra.

(Figure 2-52) Movie poster, Godzilla Against Mothra, *one-sheet.*

(Figure 2-53) Movie poster, Godzilla Against Mothra, *"speed poster."*

(Figure 2-50) Lobby card, Godzilla vs. the Thing.

(Figure 2-54) Video, Godzilla versus Mothra, *wide-screen version.*

(Figure 2-55) Window card, Godzilla vs. the Thing.

(Figure 2-56) Movie poster, All Monsters Attack.

(Figure 2-57) Movie poster, Godzilla's Revenge.

(Figure 2-58) Lobby card, King Kong Escapes.

Movie poster, *Godzilla vs. the Thing*, (with
   Mothra), U.S., 1965 . . . . $150-200
Video, *Mothra vs. Godzilla*, Japanese, blue border
   on box, Toho, 1964 (Figure 2-54). 60-75
Video, *Godzilla vs. Mothra*, Simitar wide-screen
   version, 1998 10-15
Window card, *Godzilla vs. the Thing*, yellow and
   black, 1964 (Figure 2-55) 25-40

GODZILLA'S REVENGE
(ALL MONSTERS ATTACK)
Movie poster, *All Monsters Attack*, original Japanese
   one-sheet, 1969 (Figure 2-56). 100-200
Movie poster, *Godzilla's Revenge* with *Island
   of the Burning Damned*, one-sheet,
   U.S. (Figure 2-57) 50-80

Video, *Godzilla's Revenge*, Simitar wide-screen
   version, 1998 . . . . $10-15

KING KONG ESCAPES
Lobby card, *King Kong Escapes*, Toho-Universal,
   1968, U.S., (scene dependent) (Figure 2-58) . . . 10-30
Movie poster, King Kong Escapes, one-sheet, U.S.,
   Toho-Universal, 1968 50-85

KING KONG VS. GODZILLA
Lobby card, *King Kong vs. Godzilla*, U.S., 1963,
   (scene dependent) (Figures 2-59—2-65) 30-80
Movie poster, *King Kong vs. Godzilla*, original
   Japanese one-sheet, 1962 (Figure 2-66) . . . 700-1,000
Movie poster, *King Kong vs. Godzilla*, one-sheet,
   U.S., 1963 200-250
Movie poster, *King Kong vs. Godzilla*, half-sheet
   or insert, U.S., 1963 100-150
Movie poster, *King Kong vs. Godzilla*, Japanese,
   1970 re-release 100-150

(Figure 2-68) Window card, King Kong vs. Godzilla.

(Figure 2-67) Video, King Kong vs. Godzilla.

(Figure 2-66) Movie poster, King Kong vs. Godzilla, *Japanese.*

(Figures 2-59—2-65) Lobby cards, King Kong vs. Godzilla.

69

(Figure 2-69) Movie poster, Monster Zero, *Japanese.*

(Figure 2-71) Movie poster, Monster Zero *with* War of the Gargantuas.

(Figure 2-73) Lobby card, Mothra.

(Figure 2-72) Video, Godzilla versus Monster Zero.

(Figure 2-70) Movie poster, Invasion of Astro-Monster.

(Figure 2-74) Movie poster, Mothra.

(Figure 2-75) Video, Mothra.

Movie poster, *King Kong vs. Godzilla*, Japanese,
1977 re-release $35-50
Video, *King Kong vs. Godzilla*, Japanese, blue
border on box, Toho, 1962 (Figure 2-67) 60-75
Window card, *King Kong vs. Godzilla*, 1963
(Figure 2-68) 65-120

MONSTER ZERO (INVASION OF ASTRO-MONSTER)

Movie poster, *Monster Zero*, one-sheet, Japanese,
1965 (Figure 2-69) 350-450
Movie poster, *Invasion of Astro-Monster*,
"speed poster," Japanese, 10 x 28.5 in., 1965
(Figure 2-70) 100-200
Movie poster, *Monster Zero*, one-sheet, 1966,
U.S. 150-200
Movie poster, *Monster Zero / War of the Gargantuas*,
double feature, U.S. (Figure 2-71) 30-50
Program, *Monster Zero*, Japanese, 1965 100-200
Video, *Godzilla versus Monster Zero*, Simitar
wide-screen version, 1998 (Figure 2-72) 10-15

MOTHRA (1961)

Lobby card, *Mothra*, 1961 (scene dependent)
(Figure 2-73) $10-45
Movie poster, *Mothra*, one-sheet, Japanese, 1961
(Figure 2-74) 400-500
Movie poster, *Mothra*, one-sheet, U.S. version,
1961 100-150
Video, *Mothra*, Toho, Japanese, 1961
(Figure 2-75) 60-75

MOTHRA (1996)

Movie poster, *Mothra*, one-sheet, Japanese version,
1996 20-30
Movie poster, small size, *Mothra*, Japanese version,
1996 15-20

THE MYSTERIANS

Lobby card, *Mysterians* (with Moguera), U.S.,
    1959, (scene dependent) $15-35
Movie poster, *The Mysterians,* original Japanese
    one-sheet, 1957 (Figure 2-76) 100-200
Movie poster, *The Mysterians,* one-sheet,
    U.S. version, 1959 75-125

RODAN

8 mm movies, *Rodan,* regular-sized box 25-35
8 mm home movies, *Rodan,* small box 15-25
Lobby card, *Rodan,* U.S., 1957,
    (scene dependent) 40-65
Movie poster, *Rodan,* original Japanese one-sheet,
    1956 (Figure 2-77) 300-500
Movie poster, *Rodan,* U.S. version, 1957 200-300
Video, *Rodan,* Toho, Japanese, 1956
    (Figure 2-78) 60-75

SON OF GODZILLA

Movie poster, *Son of Godzilla,* original Japanese
    one-sheet, 1967 (Figure 2-79) $150-250
Movie poster, *Son of Godzilla,* "speed poster,"
    Japanese, 10 x 28.5 in., 1967 (Figure 2-80) . 100-200
Movie poster, *Son of Godzilla,* one-sheet,
    U.S. version, 1968 130-200
Movie poster, *Son of Godzilla,* Japanese theatrical
    re-release 65-95

SYMPHONIC FANTASIA—GODZILLA

Videodisc, 2-disc set, Toho, photo cover
    (Figure 2-81) 125-160

THE TERROR OF MECHAGODZILLA
THE TERROR OF GODZILLA

Movie poster, *Terror of MechaGodzilla,* one-sheet,
    Japanese, 1975 (Figure 2-82) 75-125
Movie poster, *Terror of Godzilla,* one-sheet, U.S.,
    1977 40-75

(Figure 2-76) Movie poster, The Mysterians.

(Figure 2-77) Movie poster, Rodan.

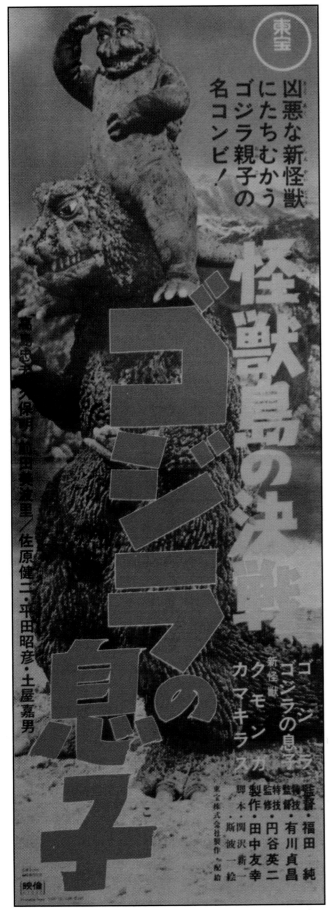

(Figure 2-79) Movie poster,
Son of Godzilla, *one-sheet.*

(Figure 2-78) Video,
Rodan.

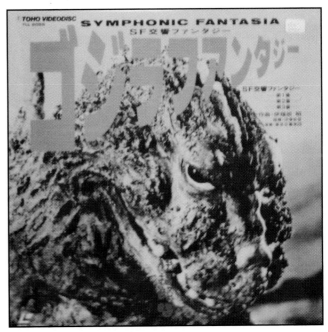

(Figure 2-81) Videodisc, Godzilla.

(Figure 2-80, left) Movie poster, Son of Godzilla,
"speed poster."

(Figure 2-82) Movie poster, Terror of MechaGodzilla.

OTHER TOHO MONSTERS

FRANKENSTEIN CONQUERS THE WORLD

Lobby card, *Frankenstein Conquers the World*,
(scene dependent) (Figure 2-83) $15-40
Super 8 mm film, *Frankenstein Conquers the World*,
black & white, AI 20-30
Movie poster, *Frankenstein Conquers the World*,
one-sheet, U.S., 1966 (Figure 2-84) 50-85
Video, *Frankenstein vs. Baragon*, Toho, Japanese,
1965 (Figure 2-85) 60-75

GORATH

Movie poster, *Gorath*, original Japanese one-sheet,
Toho, 1962 (Figure 2-86) 75-150

WAR OF THE GARGANTUAS

Video, *War of the Gargantuas*, Toho, Japanese,
1966 (Figure 2-87) $60-75

YOG! MONSTER FROM SPACE

Movie poster, *Yog! Monster from Space*, one-sheet,
U.S., 1971 (Figure 2-88) 30-50

OTHERS

Movie poster, *Legend of the Dinosaurs* and *Monster
Birds*, 1978 (Figure 2-89) 65-85

(Figure 2-84) Movie poster,
Frankenstein Conquers
the World.

(Figure 2-86) Movie poster,
Gorath.

(Figure 2-83) Lobby card, Frankenstein Conquers
the World.

(Figure 2-89) Movie poster,
Legend of the Dinosaurs
and Monster Birds.

(Figure 2-85) Video,
Frankenstein vs. Baragon.

(Figure 2-88) Movie poster,
Yog! Monster from Space.

(Figure 2-87) Video, War
of the Gargantuas.

GODZILLA

MONOGRAM

Unassembled model kit
Modèle réduit pour assembler

MOLDED IN COLOR

GLOWS IN THE DARK

English instructions included.

Notice en Français incluse.

© 1978 Toho Co., Ltd.

GODZILLA

CHAPTER THREE
MODEL KITS

ANGILAS · ANGUIRUS · ANGURUS
Kaiyodo model kit, Angilas, vinyl $75-100

BARAGON
Bandai model kit, wind-up Baragon, 1973 150-300
Billiken model kit, Baragon, vinyl 75-100
Inoue Arts model kit, Baragon, vinyl 110-130
Marusan model kit, Baragon Plamodel
    1966 2,000-6,000
Wave Metal model kit, Baragon, vinyl, 17.25 in.
    long, (shown built up) (Figures 3-1, 3-2) . . . 150-200

BATTRA
Kaiyodo model kit, Battra Larva, vinyl
    (Figure 3-3) 100-125

(Figures 3-1, 3-2) Wave Metal model kit, Baragon.

(Figure 3-3) Kaiyodo model kit, Battra Larva.

BIOLLANTE

Aoshima model kit, Biollante, 1/700 scale,
  vinyl $125-150
Kaiyodo model kit, Biollante, 1/500 scale,
  soft vinyl, discontinued 300-400

DESTROYAH · DESTROYER

Tsukuda model kit, Destroyah, 1/350 scale,
  vinyl 140-160

EBIRAH

Falchion model kit, Ebirah, 1/150 scale, vinyl . . . 75-100
Marusan model kit, Ebirah Plamodel,
  1966, very rare 4,000-8,000

FRANKENSTEIN

Monsters in Motion model kit, Frankenstein
  Conquers the World, resin 110-150

GHIDRAH · GHIDORAH · KING GHIDORAH

Aoshima model kit, King Ghidorah 1964,
  1/700 scale, metal 50-80
Aurora model kit, Monsters of the Movies series,
  1975 150-500
Bandai model kit, wind-up Ghidrah,
  1973 150-300
Hiruma Model Craft model kit,
  Ghidrah Spaceball 275-325
PAO model kit, King Ghidorah 1991 275-325

GIGAN

Inoue Arts model kit, Gigan, vinyl 110-130
Kaiyodo model kit, Gigan, resin,
  discontinued, rare early kit 100-150
Volks model kit, Gigan, resin 140-165
Wave Metal model kit, Gigan, vinyl, 12.25 in.,
  (shown built up) (Figure 3-4) 150-200

GODZILLA

Amaquest model kit, Superdeformed Godzilla 15-25
Aoshima model kit, Godzilla 1964, 1/700 scale,
  metal 60-80
Aurora model kit, Godzilla, plastic, 1964
  (Figures 3-5, 3-6) 85-500
Aurora model kit, Godzilla's Go-Cart, plastic,
  1966 650-3000
Aurora model kit, Godzilla, glow version,
  plastic, 1969 75-300
Aurora model kit, Godzilla, glow version,
  plastic, 1972 75-175
Bandai model kit, Godzilla, 4.75-in. box, 1992 8-15

(Figure 3-4) Wave Metal model kit, Gigan.

Bandai model kit, Godzilla, 1/350 scale, plastic,
  10.75 x 6.75, gray art box, (Figure 3-7) $12-20
Bandai model kit, Godzilla diorama, plastic, Kaiju
  series #11 65-90
Bandai model kit, wind-up Godzilla, 1973 150-300
Billiken model kit, Godzilla 1954, vinyl 65-95
Billiken model kit, Godzilla 1962, vinyl 50-90
Billiken model kit, Godzilla 1964, vinyl 65-95
Billiken model kit, Godzilla 1992, vinyl 85-110
Bullmark model kit, wind-up Godzilla, early
  Japanese plastic kit 1,000-3,500
Falchion model kit, Godzilla 1954, vinyl,
  21 in. tall 275-325
Hiruma Model Craft model kit, Godzilla with
  Mothra Egg diorama, resin 200-250
Hiruma Model Craft model kit,
  Godzilla Spaceball 275-325
Inoue Arts model kit, Godzilla 1962, vinyl 110-135
Kaiyodo model kit, Godzilla 1954, 1/230 scale,
  vinyl, ... 50-80
Kaiyodo model kit, Godzilla 1955, vinyl
  (Figure 3-8) 50-80
Kaiyodo model kit, Godzilla 1962, 1/250 scale,
  vinyl 50-80
Kaiyodo model kit, Godzilla 1962, vinyl, large
  version 250-275

Kaiyodo model kit, Godzilla 1964, vinyl $50-75
Kaiyodo model kit, Godzilla 1964, 1/100 scale,
    vinyl, large version 225-275
Kaiyodo model kit, Godzilla 1984, 1/250 scale,
    vinyl 70-100
Kaiyodo model kit, Godzilla 1989, 1/400 scale,
    vinyl 50-80
Kaiyodo model kit, Godzilla 1989—Jumbo,
    vinyl, 95 in. long 1,300-1,500
Kaiyodo model kit, Godzilla 1992, 1/350 scale,
    vinyl 100-120
Kaiyodo model kit, Godzilla 1993, 1/400 scale,
    vinyl 50-80
Kaiyodo model kit, Godzilla 1994, 1/400 scale,
    vinyl (Figure 3-9) 50-80

Lindberg model kit, Godzilla Super Detailed
    Model Kit, snap-fit, 7.5 in., 1995
    (Figure 3-10) $10-15
M1 model kit, Godzilla Head 1962, vinyl 375-450
M1 model kit, Godzilla Headline series,
    Godzilla 1954, (figure breaks out of egg),
    1997 60-80
M1 model kit, Godzilla Headline series,
    Godzilla 1962, (figure breaks out of egg),
    1997 60-80
M1 model kit, Godzilla Headline series,
    Godzilla 1964, (figure breaks out of egg),
    1997 60-80
M1 model kit, Godzilla Headline series,
    Godzilla 1989, (figure breaks out of egg),
    1997 60-80

(Figure 3-5) Aurora model kit, Godzilla, box.

(Figure 3-6) Aurora model kit, Godzilla, model.

(Figure 3-8) Kaiyodo model kit, Godzilla 1955.

(Figure 3-10) Lindberg model kit, Godzilla.

(Figure 3-7) Bandai model kit, Godzilla.

(Figure 3-11) M1 model kit, Godzilla 1964.

(Figure 3-9) Kaiyodo model kit, Godzilla 1994.

(Figure 3-12) M1 model kit, Godzilla from Monster Zero.

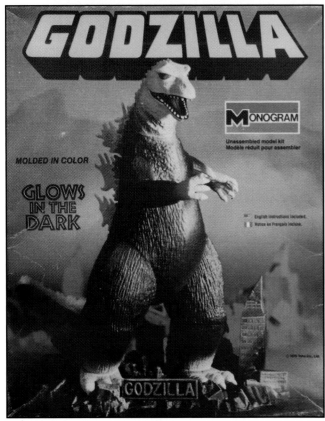

(Figure 3-13) Monogram model kit, Godzilla, from Aurora mold.

(Figure 3-14) Unmarked model kit, Godzilla.

M1 model kit, Godzilla 1964, shown built up,
19 in., 1994 (Figure 3-11) $50-75

M1 model kit, Godzilla Jumping 1965, vinyl 75-100

M1 model kit, Nagoya Castle Diorama, vinyl
and plastic, 50 pieces 175-225

M1 model kit, Godzilla skeleton,
limited edition 375-425

M1 model kit, Dancing Godzilla from *Monster
Zero*, 1/400 scale, 10 x 8.5-in. box
(Figure 3-12) 60-80

Mad Lab model kit, Superdeformed Stomping
Godzilla, resin, 3.5 in., 1991 20-30

Marusan model kit, Godzilla Plamodel,
1964 4,000-7,000

Marusan model kit, Giant Godzilla Plamodel,
1967 3,000-9,000

Max Factory model kit, Godzilla 1992, vinyl 60-80

Monogram model kit, Godzilla, plastic,
from Aurora mold, discontinued, 1970s
(Figure 3-13) 60-85

Tsukuda model kit, Godzilla 1964, 1/160 scale,
vinyl 125-150

Volks model kit, Godzilla 1989, resin $275-325
Volks model kit, Godzilla 1993, resin 100-150
Unmarked model kit, Godzilla stands over city
    base, about 4.5 in., unmarked (Figure 3-14) ... 25-35
Unmarked model kit, Superdeformed Godzilla,
    off-white resin, unmarked 15-35

KING KONG
Astro Zombies model kit, Toho's King Kong 75-100

MANDA
Paradise model kit, Manda diorama, vinyl 275-325

MECHAGODZILLA · SUPER MECHAGODZILLA
Bandai model kit, Super MechaGodzilla, 1/600 scale,
    14.25 x 9.25-in. box, 1993 (Figure 3-15) 35-50
Bandai model kit, wind-up MechaGodzilla,
    1974 150-300
Kaiyodo model kit, MechaGodzilla 1993, vinyl ... 50-75
Max Factory model kit, MechaGodzilla 1993,
    vinyl 50-75
Volks model kit, MechaGodzilla 1974, resin,
    Volks 125-150

MINYA · BABY GODZILLA · LITTLE GODZILLA · GODZILLA JR.
Kaiyodo model kit, Godzilla Jr. $100-150
Marusan model kit, Hatching Minya Plamodel,
    1960s 800-2,000
Unmarked model Kit, Minya, resin, 3.5 in.,
    (Figure 3-16) 20-35
Unmarked model kit, Tadzilla
    (old style Minya, waving), resin, 10 in. 70-90

MOGUERA · MOGERA · M.O.G.U.E.R.A.
Aoshima model kit, Moguera, 1/72 scale,
    vinyl 75-100
Kaiyodo model kit, Moguera, resin, small size ... 85-115

MOTHRA
Aoshima model kit, Mothra 1964, 1/700 scale,
    metal 55-85
Hiruma Model Craft model kit, Mothra Larva,
    resin, ... 55-85
Paradise model kit, Mothra Adult, vinyl 200-250
Volks model kit, Mothra Adult, resin 125-150
Wave Metal model kit, Mothra Larva, vinyl 125-45

(Figure 3-15) Bandai model kit, Super MechaGodzilla.

(Figure 3-16) Unmarked model kit, Minya.

(Figure 3-17) Aurora model kit, Rodan.

(Figure 3-18) Tsukuda model kit, Rodan.

RODAN

Aurora model kit, Monsters of the Movies series,
  plastic, 1975 (Figure 3-17) $150-500
Hiruma Model Craft model kit,
  Rodan Spaceball 275-325
Paradise model kit, Rodan, vinyl 325-375
Tsukuda model kit, Rodan, 1/160 scale, vinyl,
  1994 (Figure 3-18) 80-120

SPACE GODZILLA

Kaiyodo model kit, Space Godzilla, resin,
  large size 200-250
Kaiyodo model kit, Space Godzilla, resin,
  small size 85-110

GROUP SHOTS AND TAG TEAMS

Kaiyodo model kit, Ghidrah Diorama (with
  Mothra, Rodan, Godzilla), resin $500-750
Kaiyodo model kit, Godzilla vs. Biollante,
  diorama 1,000-1,400
Kaiyodo model kit, King Kong vs. Godzilla,
  early resin kit, discontinued 125-175
Paradise model kit, Godzilla swings Ebirah
  diorama, vinyl 250-300
Paradise model kit, King Kong swings Godzilla
  diorama, vinyl 250-300
Wave Metal model kit, Godzilla and Jet-Jaguar,
  vinyl 25-45
Wave Metal model kit, Godzilla and Ebirah,
  vinyl 40-65

CHAPTER FOUR
TOYS & GAMES

ANGILAS

Die-cast figure, Angilas, Bullmark, boxed, 1970s,
  rare $400-900

BARAGON

Die-cast figure, Baragon, green and gold version,
  4.5 in., Bullmark, boxed, 1970s 100-200
Die-cast figure, Baragon, blue version, 4.5 in.,
  Bullmark, boxed, 1970s (Figure 4-1) 125-225
Tin toy, Baragon, wire remote control, 11 in.,
  Marusan, 1966 1,000-3,500
Tin toy, Baragon, with string remote control,
  11 in., from Marusan mold, Bullmark,
  early 1970s (Figure 4-2) 600-1,000

(Figure 4-2) Baragon tin toy.

(Figure 4-1, left) Die-cast Baragon figure.

(Figure 4-4) Action Walking Ghidorah.

(Figure 4-5) Bendable Ghidorah figure.

(Figure 4-3) Superdeformed Destroyah suction cup toy.

DESTROYAH · DESTROYER

Suction cup toy, Superdeformed Destroyah, 1.5 in.
    with cup, 1995 (Figure 4-3) $4-8
Walking Destroyer, roars, 11 in., Bandai, 1995   . 120-165

GHIDRAH · GHIDORAH · KING GHIDORAH · MECHAGHIDORAH

Battery-op Action Walking Ghidorah, roars, moves
    wings, Trendmasters, 1994 (Figure 4-4) 20-40
Bendable figure, Ghidrah, 4 in., Trendmasters,
    1994 (Figure 4-5) 3-6
Bendee, Godzilla trading card premium,
    Yamakatsu, 1983, rare 85-110
Die-cast figure, die-cast and plastic, 6 in., Bullmark,
    boxed, 1977-1978 (Figures 4-6, 4-7) 200-400
Hatching egg, mechanical plastic toy, 3.5-in. egg
    with Ghidrah inside, Takara, 1988 20-35
Hatching Monster Ghidorah, breaks out of
    plastic egg, Trendmasters, 1994 4-10
Lego Mini King Ghidrah, Kawada,
    8.5 x 5.5-in. box, 1995 (Figure 4-8) 18-30
Lego King Ghidrah, large size, photo on box,
    8.25 x 11 in., Kawada, 1995 (Figure 4-9) 55-70
Mad Ball, MechaGhidrah, 7-in. circumference,
    Bandai, in small plastic case, 1996 (Figure 4-10) . 5-10
Wind-up walker, MechaGhidorah, Trendmasters,
    1994 3-6

(Figure 4-6) Die-cast
Ghidorah figure, in box.

(Figure 4-7) Die-cast
Ghidorah figure.

(Figure 4-10) Mad Ball, MechaGhidrah.

(Figure 4-9) Lego King Ghidrah.

(Figure 4-8) Lego Mini King Ghidrah.

(Figure 4-11) Die-cast Gigan figure.

GIGAN

Die-cast figure, 4.5 in., Gigan, Bullmark, boxed,
    1970s (Figure 4-11) $200-400
Tin toy, Gigan, with string remote control,
    battery-op, Bullmark, 1972 2,000-3,500

GODZILLA

Battery-op Action Walking Godzilla, walks and roars,
    Trendmasters, 1994 (Figures 4-12, 4-13) 15-40
Battery-op Blasting Attack Godzilla, walks,
    fins light up, Bandai 150-200
Battery-op DX Godzilla, moving version of
    1992 Godzilla, Bandai 75-100
Battery-op Godzilla, Bandai Real Hobby Series,
    boxed 325-375
Battery-op toy, unlicensed, walks, breathes smoke,
    roars, New Bright, 1987 (Figure 4-14) 20-30
Battery-op toy, unlicensed, green fur, eyes glow,
    walks, 11 in., Korea, Jamina, 1987
    (Figure 4-15) 15-25
Battery-op toy, unlicensed, eyes glow, walks, green
    and silver plastic, 5.25 in., Taiwan
    (Figure 4-16) 10-15
Battery-op toy, unlicensed, with string remote
    control, Radio Shack (Figure 4-17) 8-12

Battery-op Walking Godzilla, rubber body, vinyl tail,
    roars, 11 in., Bandai, 1994 (Figure 4-18) . . . $100-150
Battery-op Walking Meltdown Godzilla,
    (Heat Walk Godzilla), glows, Bandai, 1995
    (Figure 4-19) 125-175
Bendable figure, 4 in., Trendmasters, 1994
    (Figures 4-20, 4-21) 3-6
Bendee, Kaiju series Godzilla, 1983 125-175
Bendee, Godzilla trading card premium,
    Yamakatsu, 1983, rare 85-110
Bop bag, Inflatable 48-in. Godzilla bop bag,
    Imperial, 1985 20-30
Bubble Blowing Godzilla, Imperial,
    9.25 x 6.75-in. box, 1985 (Figure 4-22) 25-40
Candy dispenser, Godzilla head on "collectible candy
    machine," 5.5 in., Flix, bagged, 1990s
    (Figure 4-23) 12-20
Clip-on Godzilla hands, green plastic, 3.5 in.,
    unlicensed, Korea 4-7
Coloring book, Godzilla—King of the Monsters,
    Resource Publications # 630, 1977 35-45
Combat Joe Godzilla set, vinyl with 12-in.
    Combat Joe figure, 1984 600-1000
Computer game, Godzilla, for IBM, 1993 75-100
Computer game, Godzilla, King of the Monsters,
    hand-held, Micro Games of America, carded,
    1990s (Figure 4-24) 10-15
Die-cast figure, Godzilla, green version,
    stomach holds weapons, 4.5 in., boxed, Bullmark,
    1970s (Figure 4-25) 50-150
Die-cast figure, Godzilla, brown version,
    stomach holds weapons, 4.5 in., boxed,
    Bullmark, 1970s 75-175

(Figure 4-18) Walking Godzilla.

(Figure 4-13) Action Walking Godzilla.

(Figure 4-12) Action Walking Godzilla, box.

(Figure 4-15) Battery-operated Godzilla, green fur.

(Figure 4-14) Battery-operated Godzilla, breathes smoke.

(Figure 4-16) Battery-operated Godzilla, green and silver plastic.

(Figure 4-23) Godzilla candy dispenser.

(Figure 4-17) Battery-operated Godzilla, with string remote control.

Inflatable Godzilla, Giant 8 ft. Inflatable Godzilla, Imperial, 1985 . . . . $60-80

Inflatable Godzilla, Giant 12 ft. Inflatable Godzilla, Imperial, 1985 100-125

Inflatable Godzilla figure, 8.5 in., Midori PWA, no year marked (Figure 4-36) 15-25

Jump Up figure, Godzilla, Trendmasters, 1994 (Figure 4-37) 3-6

King of the Monsters, boxed set with large Godzilla figure and tank, 16 x 19 in., Bandai, 1993 (Figure 4-38) 200-300

Mad Ball, 7-in. circumference, Bandai, in small plastic case, 1996 5-9

Magic Rocks, includes paintable Godzilla figure, Crafthouse, 1995 (Figure 4-39) 15-25

"Monster Dinosaur," unlicensed, Pull Back and Go Action, China, Kids Goods (Figure 4-40) 8-12

Plush toy, Hanna-Barbera *Godzilla Power Hour* tie-in., 8.5 in., Knickerbocker, 1979 (Figure 4-41) 75-100

Plush toy, Tokyo Giants Baseball Team, Godzilla (#55), 8.25 in., in poly bag, Matsui (Figure 4-42) 15-25

Puzzle, Godzilla, 150 pieces, 10 x 14 in., HG Toys, 1975 (Figure 4-43) 25-45

Puzzle, Godzilla—King of the Creatures, APC, 1978 . . . . $20-30

Radio-controlled Godzilla 1954, walks, moves head and tail, roars, 21 in., Tokyo Marui 750-900

Radio-controlled Godzilla 1989, walks, moves head and tail, roars, 21 in., Tokyo Marui 750-900

Rifle, Godzilla Raids Again toy rifle, 1950s 400-700

Rolling Godzilla, Superdeformed series, Yutaka . . . 20-30

Shogun Warriors Godzilla, olive green version, shoots hand, 19 in., Toho Co., Mattel, 1977 (Figures 4-44, 4-45) 75-175

Shogun Warriors Godzilla, brighter green version, shoots hand, 19 in., Toho Co., Mattel, 1977 . 100-200

Snapper toy, Superdeformed Godzilla, plastic, 3 in., boxed, Bandai (Figure 4-46) 15-25

Sparker friction toy, green plastic, poseable arms, no mark, 1.75 in., Takara (Figure 4-47) 10-20

Sparker friction toy, same as above, in costume (bride, etc.) 20-30

Sparker toy, twist arm and mouth sparks, Bullmark, very rare 800-1,200

Sparkzilla, wind-up sparker toy, 3 in., Accouterments/Archie McPhee, 1994 (Figure 4-48) 3-8

Squeak toy, green and yellow felt finish, no mark, 2 in. (Figure 4-49) 15-25

(Figure 4-19) Walking Meltdown Godzilla.

(Figure 4-20) Bendable Godzilla figure, in box.

(Figure 4-21) Bendable Godzilla figure.

(Figure 4-25) Die-cast Godzilla figure, green version.

(Figure 4-22) Bubble Blowing Godzilla.

(Figure 4-26) Godzilla Game, by Mattel.

(Figure 4-28) Figure from Godzilla Attacks New York Playset.

(Figure 4-27) Godzilla Attacks New York Playset.

(Figure 4-24) Hand-held computer game.

(Figure 4-29) Growing Godzilla.

(Figure 4-30) Gymnast Godzilla.

(Figure 4-32) Hatching Godzilla, plush.

(Figure 4-33) Hatching Godzilla, mechanical plastic toy.

(Figure 4-34) Inflatable Godzilla baseball bat.

(Figure 4-31) Hatching Monsters Godzilla, Trendmasters.

(Figure 4-35) Inflatable Godzilla, 6 ft.

(Figure 4-36) Inflatable Godzilla, 8.5 in.

(Figure 4-37) Jump Up Godzilla figure.

(Figure 4-38) King of the Monsters boxed set.

Squirt gun, plastic figural, 7.5 in., Chinese, unlicensed,
    Acute Force, in poly bag (Figure 4-50) $8-15
Squirt gun, blue plastic, with Godzilla on top,
    7 in., Japan (Figure 4-51) 15-22
Squirt toy, White Castle premium 12-18
Stickers, Godzilla Power Hour puffy stickers, full
    sheet, 11 x 7 in., Hanna-Barbera, 1979 8-12
Suction cup toy, Superdeformed Godzilla,
    1.5 in. with cup, 1995 (Figure 4-52) 4-8
Suction cup toy, Superdeformed Meltdown Godzilla,
    1.5 in. with cup, 1995 (Figure 4-53) 4-8
Talking Godzilla, with pull string for roar, plastic,
    17.5 in. tall, Popy (Figure 4-54) 1,200-2,000

Tin Godzilla, wire remote control, 11 in.,
    Marusan, 1966 . . . . $1,000-3,500
Tin toy, with string remote control, 11 in.,
    from Marusan mold, Bullmark,
    early 1970s (Figure 4-55) 600-1,000
Tin wind-up, Godzilla with Mothra at his tail,
    Billiken, 1990s 100-150

(Figure 4-40) "Monster Dinosaur," unlicensed.

(Figure 4-41) Plush toy, Godzilla Power Hour tie-in.

(Figure 4-39) Magic Rocks with Godzilla figure.

(Figure 4-42) Plush toy, Tokyo Giants.

(Figure 4-43) Godzilla puzzle.

(Figure 4-44) Shogun Warriors Godzilla, box.

(Figure 4-45) Shogun Warriors Godzilla.

(Figure 4-46) Snapper toy, Superdeformed Godzilla.

(Figure 4-47) Sparker friction Godzilla toy.

(Figure 4-49) Godzilla squeak toy.

(Figure 4-48) Sparkzilla.

(Figure 4-50) Godzilla figural squirt gun.

(Figure 4-51) Squirt gun with Godzilla on top.

(Figure 4-52) Superdeformed Godzilla suction cup toy.

(Figure 4-53) Superdeformed Meltdown Godzilla suction cup toy.

(Figure 4-55) Godzilla tin toy.

(Figure 4-56) Wind-up Godzilla, tin.

(Figure 4-57) Wind-up sparking Godzilla.

(Figure 4-54) Talking Godzilla.

(Figure 4-58) Wind-up Godzilla, Japanese.

(Figure 4-59) Wind-up Godzilla, Bandai.

(Figure 4-60) Wind-up Godzilla, Trendmasters.

(Figure 4-61) Battery-operated MechaGodzilla.

(Figure 4-62) Bendable
MechaGodzilla.

(Figure 4-63) Bendable
MechaGodzilla, in box.

(Figure 4-64) Die-cast
MechaGodzilla figure, box.

(Figure 4-65) Die-cast
MechaGodzilla figure.

Tin wind-up Godzilla, green version, walks,
    swings arms, 7 in., boxed, Billiken, 1990s . . . $100-150
Tin wind-up Godzilla, brown version, same as
    above, Billiken (Figure 4-56) 75-125
View-Master, reel set,
    "Godzilla—Godzilla's Rampage," GAF 20-30
View-Master, talking View-Master reels, "Godzilla—
    Godzilla's Rampage," GAF 20-30
White Castle premium, complete set 35-50
Wind-up sparking walker, yellow and green with red
    winder, 3.25 in., Hong Kong (Figure 4-57) 3-8
Wind-up walker, Godzilla, 2 in., Japanese,
    ca., 1970s (Figure 4-58) 12-20
Wind-up walker, blue plastic, 3 in., Godzilla is Go
    series, Bandai, 1994 (Figure 4-59) 8-15
Wind-up walker, Godzilla, Trendmasters,
    1994 (Figure 4-60) 3-6

MECHAGODZILLA

Battery-op MechaGodzilla 1988, giant size,
    16-in. figure, 20-in. box, Bandai, 1993
    (Figure 4-61) $200-300
Bendable figure, MechaGodzilla, 4 in.,
    Trendmasters, 1994 (Figures 4-62, 4-63) 3-6
Die-cast figure, MechaGodzilla, yellow plastic
    knobs on knees, 4.5 in., Bullmark, boxed,
    1970s (Figures 4-64, 4-65) 150-300
Die-cast figure, MechaGodzilla, black "belt"
    with painted name, 4.5 in., Popy, 1970s
    (Figure 4-66) 200-400
Hatching Monsters MechaGodzilla, breaks out of
    plastic egg, Trendmasters, 1994 4-10
Jump Up figure, MechaGodzilla, Trendmasters,
    1994 (Figure 4-67) 3-6

(Figure 4-66) Die-cast MechaGodzilla figure, with painted name.

(Figure 4-67) Jump Up MechaGodzilla figure.

(Figure 4-69) Wind-up MechaGodzilla.

(Figure 4-70) Mad Ball, Minya.

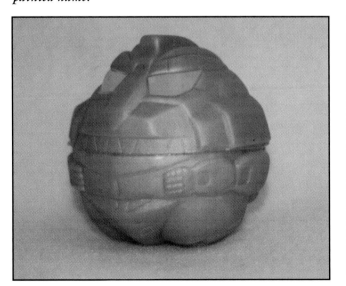

(Figure 4-68) Mad Ball, MechaGodzilla.

(Figure 4-72) Bendable Mothra figure.

(Figure 4-71) Battery-operated Mothra.

(Figure 4-75) Hatching egg with Rodan inside.

(Figure 4-73) Mad Ball, Mothra Adult.

(Figure 4-74) Mad Ball, Mothra Larva.

Lego MechaGodzilla, 8.25 x 5.5-in. box,
    Kawada, 1995 . . . . $20-30
Mad Ball, MechaGodzilla, 7-in. circumference,
    Bandai, in small plastic case, 1996 (Figure 4-68) . 5-10
Wind-up walker, MechaGodzilla, Trendmasters,
    1994 (Figure 4-69) 3-6

MINYA · BABY GODZILLA · LITTLE GODZILLA
Mad Ball, Minya, 7 in. circumference, Bandai, in
    small plastic case, 1996 (Figure 4-70) 5-10

MOTHRA
Battery-op Mothra DX, larva, creeps, moves, Bandai,
    12 x 3.25-in. box, 1996 (Figure 4-71) 35-45
Bendable figure, Mothra, Trendmasters, 1994
    (Figure 4-72) 3-6

Hatching egg, mechanical plastic toy, egg with
Mothra inside, 3.5 in., Takara, 1988 . . . . $25-40
Hatching Monsters Mothra, breaks out of plastic
egg, Trendmasters, 1994 4-10
Mad Ball, Mothra Adult, 7-in. circumference,
Bandai, in small plastic case, 1996 (Figure 4-73) . 5-10
Mad Ball, Mothra Larva, 7-in. circumference,
Bandai, in small plastic case, 1996 (Figure 4-74) . 5-10
Radio-controlled Mothra Larva, moves, shoots
silly string from mouth, Tokyo Marui, 1994 . . 550-700
Swing mascot, Superdeformed Mothra on suction
cup wire, Japanese, 1990s 12-20
Tin wind-up Mothra Adult, Billiken, boxed,
1990s 50-100

RODAN

Bendable figure, Rodan, 4 in., Trendmasters, 1994 . . 3-6
Hatching egg, mechanical plastic toy, 3.5-in. egg with
Rodan inside, Takara, 1988 (Figure 4-75) 20-35
Hatching Monsters Rodan, breaks out of plastic egg,
Trendmasters, 1994 4-10
Mattel's World's Greatest Monsters series, Rodan,
38-in. wingspan, 10 x 19.5-in. box, 1979
(Figures 4-76, 4-77) 150-350
Wind-up walker, Rodan, Trendmasters, 1994 3-6

SPACE GODZILLA

Suction cup toy, Superdeformed Space Godzilla, 1.5 in.
with cup, 1995 4-8

GROUP SHOTS AND PLAYSETS

Figure Maker Set; Godzilla, Rodan, and
MechaGhidorah; RoseArt, 1994 (Figure 4-78) . . 18-25
Lego toys; Godzilla, Ghidrah, and MechaGodzilla
group shot; Kawada, 1995, each (Figure 4-79) . . 20-30

(Figure 4-76) Rodan, World's Greatest Monsters series.

Micro Battle Playset, Godzilla vs. Ghidorah in San
Francisco, Trendmasters, 1994 . . . . $4-8
Micro Battle Playset, Godzilla vs. MechaGodzilla in
Los Angeles, Trendmasters, 1994 (Figure 4-80) . . . 4-8
Micro Battle Playset, Godzilla vs. Rodan in
New York City, Trendmasters, 1994 (Figure 4-81) . 4-8
Slot machine toy, Godzilla vs. Mothra, Toho Eiga,
8 x 3.5-in. box (Figure 4-82) 20-25
Stamp Set, seven superdeformed figural stamps,
1.5 in. tall, Bandai, 7.75 x 8.75-in. box, 1994
(Figure 4-83) 18-25

OTHERS
JIRAS (ULTRAMAN)

*(Note: Jiras was made from putting a frill around the neck of
the Godzilla costume . . .)*

Tin toy, with string remote control, battery-op,
11 in., Bullmark (Figure 4-84) 800-1,000

*(Figure 4-77) Rodan,
World's Greatest Monsters
series, box.*

(Figure 4-79) Godzilla, Ghidrah, and MechaGodzilla Lego Set.

(Figure 4-80) Micro Battle Playset, Godzilla vs. MechaGodzilla in Los Angeles.

(Figure 4-81) Micro Battle Playset, Godzilla vs. Rodan in New York City.

(Figure 4-78) Figure Maker Set, with Rodan and MechaGhidorah.

(Figure 4-83) Japanese stamp set.

(Figure 4-82) Slot machine toy, Godzilla vs. Mothra.

(Figure 4-84) Jiras tin toy.

CHAPTER FIVE
BOOKS, CARDS, & MUSIC
INCLUDING MAGAZINES & COMICS

BOOKS

All About Godzilla, yellow with cartoon in corner,
  8.5 x 10 in., Grakken, 1993 (Figure 5-1) $20-30

Art of Godzilla vs. Mothra, The, hardback,
  10.5 x 8.5 in. (Figure 5-2) 40-55

Godzilla and MechaGodzilla on the cover,
  Japanese 15-25

Godzilla and Mothra on cover with "Peanut Sisters"
  inset, Vol. 2, 12 x 8.25 in., Japanese
  (Figure 5-3) 8-12

Godzilla, First—1954-1955, by Osamu Kishikawa,
  hardback, 12 x 8.5 in., Japanese (Figure 5-4) . . 35-50

Godzilla, Second—1962-1964, by Osamu Kishikawa,
  hardback, 12 x 8.5 in., Japanese (Figure 5-5) . . 35-50

Godzilla, King of the Monsters, by Robert Marrero,
  soft cover, 8.5 x 11 in., Fantasma Books,
  1996 (Figure 5-6) 16-25

Godzilla 1985, hardback, green art with red title
  banner, 12 x 8.5 in., Japanese (Figure 5-7) 10-20

Godzilla vs. Mothra, cardboard picture book,
  10.25 x 7.5 in., Japanese, 1992 5-10

Graph Book Godzilla, 8.25 x 10 in., Kodansha,
  1983 (Figure 5-8) 35-45

Great Guide to Japanese SFX Monsters, 6 x 4.25 in.,
  Akita Shoten, 1985 (Figure 5-9) 8-15

Japanese Children's Books, 8.5 x 7.25 in.,
  various titles, mid-1980s (shown: *Godzilla vs.
  MechaGodzilla*) (Figure 5-10) 25-35

Monsters Are Attacking Tokyo, by Stuart
  Galbraith IV, soft cover, 8 x 10 in., Feral House,
  1998 (Figure 5-11) 15-20

Official Godzilla Compendium, by J.D. Lees and
  Marc Cerasini, soft cover, Random House, 1998
  (Figure 5-12) 13-17

Photo novel, *Godzilla vs. the Thing*, soft cover,
  green title on bottom cover, 7.25 x 5 in. $20-30

Photo novel, *Godzilla vs. the Sea Monster*, soft cover,
  green title on bottom cover, 7.25 x 5 in. 20-30

Photo novel, *Godzilla vs. MechaGodzilla*, soft cover,
  green title on bottom cover, 7.25 x 5 in.
  (Figure 5-13) 20-30

Photo novel, *Ghidrah*, soft cover,
  green title on bottom cover, 7.25 x 5 in. 20-30

(Figure 5-1) Book, All About Godzilla.

(Figure 5-4) Book, Godzilla—First 1954-1955.

(Figure 5-5) Book, Godzilla—Second 1962-1964.

(Figure 5-2) Book, The Art of Godzilla vs. Mothra.

(Figure 5-3) Japanese book, Godzilla and Mothra on the cover.

(Figure 5-10) Japanese children's book.

(Figure 5-8) Graph Book Godzilla.

(Figure 5-9) Great Guide to Japanese SFX Monsters.

(Figure 5-6) Book, Godzilla, King of the Monsters.

(Figure 5-7, right) Book, Godzilla 1985.

(Figure 5-13) Book, Godzilla vs. MechaGodzilla.

(Figure 5-17) Book, Special Effects Movies: 1954-1994.

(Figure 5-11) Book, Monsters Are Attacking Tokyo.

(Figure 5-12) Book, **Official Godzilla Compendium.**

(Figure 5-14) Book, Godzilla vs. Destroyah.

COMIC BOOKS

GODZILLA, KING OF THE MONSTERS,

Marvel Comics Group, August 1977—July 1979

(Figure 5-18) Godzilla, King of the Monsters, *Marvel, #7.*

(Figure 5-19) Godzilla, King of the Monsters, *Marvel, #11.*

(Figure 5-15) Book, Godzilla vs. MechaGodzilla.

(Figure 5-16) Book, Godzilla vs. Space Godzilla.

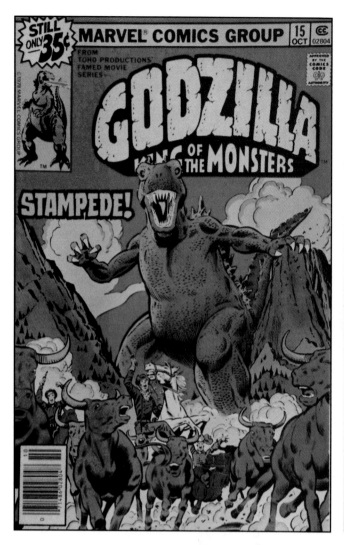

(Figure 5-20) Godzilla, King of the Monsters, Marvel, #15.

(Figure 5-21) Godzilla, King of the Monsters, Marvel, #16.

(Figure 5-22) Godzilla, King of the Monsters, Marvel, #18.

(Figure 5-23) Godzilla, King of the Monsters, Marvel, #19.

(Figure 5-24) Godzilla, King of the Monsters, Marvel, #20.

(Figure 5-25) Godzilla, King of the Monsters, Marvel, #21.

GODZILLA

**Dark Horse Comics, limited series, black and white,
1988**

GODZILLA, KING OF THE MONSTERS

Dark Horse Comics, May 1995—present

JICC (JAPANESE COMICS)

OTHER JAPANESE COMICS

(Figure 5-28) Godzilla vs. Hero Zero *comic book.*

(Figure 5-29) Comic art portfolio, Mignola art on cover.

(Figure 5-26) Godzilla, King of the Monsters, *Marvel, #22.*

(Figure 5-27) Godzilla, King of the Monsters, *Marvel, #23.*

(Figure 5-30) Comic art portfolio, Adams art on cover.

(Figure 5-31) Godzilla, King of the Monsters, *Dark Horse, #7.*

(*Figure 5-33*) Godzilla Comic Counterattack.

(*Figure 5-32*) The Godzilla Comic.

(*Figure 5-34*) Godzilla vs. the Sea Monster.

(*Figure 5-35*) Godzilla vs. MechaGodzilla Warbook.

MAGAZINES

CULT MOVIES & VIDEO

Cult Movies & Video, cover story, issue #7, 1990s . . $4-8

FAMOUS MONSTERS OF FILMLAND

Famous Monsters magazine, *Frankenstein Conquers the World* cover story, issue #39 10-15

Famous Monsters magazine, 100-page special on Japan's Monsters, issue #114 45-75

Famous Monsters magazine, Godzilla vs. Bionic Monster cover, issue #135 15-20

FANGORIA

Fangoria magazine, cover story, 25 Years with Godzilla, issue #1 (Figure 5-36) 30-50

G-FAN

#1 20-30
#2 15-20
#3 15-20
#4 15-20
#5 15-20

#6 . . . . $15-20
#7, Newsletter style cover, banner says "Daikaiju Society of North America" 15-20
#8 10-15
#9, Godzilla fights sea serpent on cover 10-15
#10 20-25
#11, Godzilla vs. King Ghidorah on cover, Sept./Oct. 1994 (Figure 5-37) 5-8

(Figure 5-37) **G-Fan** *magazine, #11.*

(Figure 5-36) **Fangoria** *magazine, premiere issue.*

(Figure 5-38) G-Fan *magazine, #12.*

(Figure 5-39) G-Fan *magazine, #17.*

(Figure 5-40) G-Fan *magazine, #18.*

(Figure 5-41) G-Fan *magazine, #19.*

(Figure 5-42) G-Fan *magazine, #21.*

(Figure 5-43) G-Fan *magazine, #23.*

(Figure 5-44) G-Fan *magazine, #24.*

(Figure 5-45) G-Fan *magazine, #26.*

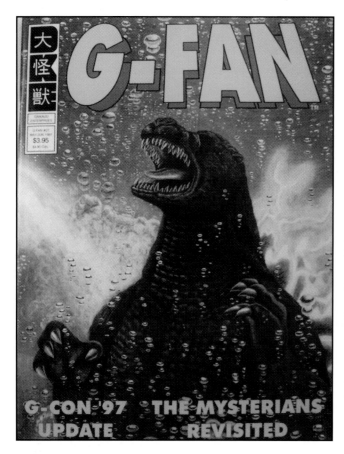

(Figure 5-46) G-Fan *magazine, #27.*

(Figure 5-47) G-Fan *magazine, #28.*

(Figure 5-48) G-Fan *magazine, #29.*

(Figure 5-49) G-Fan *magazine, #30.*

(Figure 5-51) G-Fan *magazine, #32.*

(Figure 5-52) G-Fan Special Collection #1.

(Figure 5-50) G-Fan *magazine, #31.*

(Figure 5-53) Kaiju Fan *magazine, #5.*

(Figure 5-54) Kaiju Fan *magazine, #8.*

(Figure 5-55) Monster Times, #26.

(Figure 5-56) Monster Times, #35.

MONSTER TIMES

MONSTERS OF THE MOVIES

ORIENTAL CINEMA

SCARY MONSTERS

MARKALITE, THE MAGAZINE OF JAPANESE FANTASY

MONSTERLAND (FORREST J ACKERMAN'S MONSTERLAND)

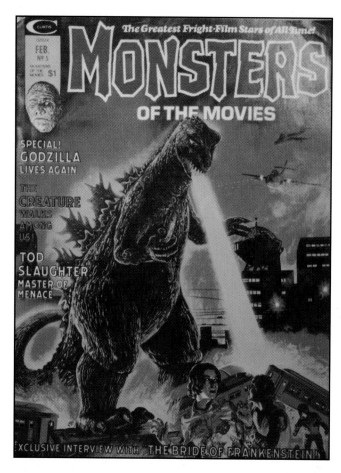

(Figure 5-58) Monsters of the Movies, #5, *Godzilla on cover.*

TRADING CARDS

GODZILLA, TRADING COLLECTION, JAPANESE IMPORT, 1990S

Set features 114 cards, including normal, laser, and 3-D holographic designs.

Full set	$20-30
Individual card (Figure 5-59)	25¢
Laser card	1-2
3-D holographic card	2-5
Empty box (Figure 5-60)	1-2

GODZILLA, CHROMIUM TRADING CARDS, AMADA, 1996

Set features 54 cards, all chromium.

Full set (shown: individual card) (Figure 5-61)	20-30
Wax pack (Figure 5-62)	2-3
Full box	50

KING KONG, TRADING CARD SET, DONRUSS, 1965

This fun set features black and white photos with white borders, accented with funny quotes in word bubbles.

(Figure 5-57) Monster Times Special #3, *"First Giant Collectors Edition."*

Some say "Write In Your Own." The set is comprised of a total of 55 cards (note: there is no card #16) and includes RKO and Toho Kong. The backs fit together to make a big color picture.

Full set	$375-425
Individual card (Figure 5-63)	6-7
Empty box	100-125
Unopened pack	55-70
Wrapper	25-30

OTHER CARD SETS

Boxed card set, Godzilla vs. Ghidrah on box cover, Japanese (Figure 5-64)	15-25
Japanese wax pack, full-color shot of Godzilla on cover, with staples (Figure 5-65)	2-4

*(Figure 5-59) Megalon trading card from the
Trading Collection.*

*(Figure 5-62) Godzilla Chromium Trading
Cards wax pack.*

(Figure 5-60) Trading Collection, set of Godzilla trading cards.

(Figure 5-61) Godzilla card from the Godzilla Chromium Trading Card set.

(Figure 5-63) Trading card from King Kong trading card set.

(Figure 5-64) Japanese boxed trading card set.

MISCELLANEOUS PAPER PRODUCTS

Godzilla cardboard mini-poster set, boxed,
 7.5 x 5.25 in., 1984 . . . . $20-30
Godzilla poster pen set, with colored pens,
 20 x 14 in., 1990s 4-8

Godzilla—Monster Comes Back! Special Poster Book,
 16 cardboard pin-ups, 10.25 x 14.5 in.,
 Japanese, 1984 (Figures 5-66, 5-67) $20-35
30th Anniversary boxed set of Godzilla paper items,
 posters, ads, etc., Japanese, 1984
 (Figure 5-68) 200-400
Stickers, Godzilla 3-D stickers, based on
 Hanna-Barbera cartoon, 1979 (Figure 5-69) . . 10-15

RECORDS, CDS, MUSIC

CD, *Godzilla 1954*, Toho EMI, 1993
 (Figure 5-70) 25-35
CD, *Godzilla 1984*, Toho EMI, 1993
 (Figure 5-71) 25-35
CD, *Godzilla vs. Destroyah*, Toho, 1995
 (Figure 5-72) 30-40
CD, *Godzilla vs. MechaGodzilla*, Toho EMI, 1993
 (Figure 5-73) 35-45
CD, *Godzilla vs. Mothra*, Toshiba EMI, 1992
 (Figure 5-74) 35-45
CD, *Howl: The Grunts and Growls of All Toho
 Monsters*, Sony Records, 1992 (Figure 5-75) . . . 25-35
CD, *The Monster Movie Music Album*, Silva Screen,
 1998 (Figure 5-76) 25-35
CD single, "Mothra's Song," 3.5 x 6.5 in., Toho,
 1992 (Figure 5-77) 12-20
Record LP, *Godzilla King of the Monsters*,
 two new adventures, Wonderland, 1970s
 (Figure 5-78) 20-30
Record, 45 RPM, "March of the Monsters,"
 Capitol Records 40-60

(Figure 5-66) Godzilla— Monster Comes Back!

(Figure 5-67) Godzilla— Monster Comes Back! *poster.*

(Figure 5-65) Japanese wax pack of trading cards, Godzilla on cover.

(Figure 5-69) Godzilla 3-D stickers.

(Figure 5-68) 30th Anniversary boxed set of Godzilla paper items.

(Figure 5-70) Godzilla 1954, *CD.*

(Figure 5-71) Godzilla 1984, *CD.*

(Figure 5-72) Godzilla vs. Destroyah, *CD.*

(Figure 5-73) Godzilla vs. MechaGodzilla, *CD.*

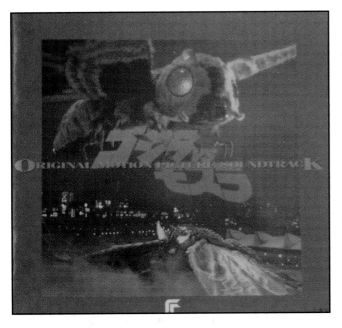

(Figure 5-74) Godzilla vs. Mothra, *CD.*

(Figure 5-75) Howl: The Grunts and Growls of All Toho Monsters, *CD.*

(Figure 5-78) Godzilla, King of the Monsters, *LP.*

(Figure 5-77) "Mothra's Song," *CD single.*

(Figure 5-76) **The Monster Movie Music Album,** *CD.*

CHAPTER SIX

GODZILLA AROUND THE HOUSE
CLOTHES & EVERYDAY ITEMS

GODZILLA

Ash tray, Godzilla, ceramic, squirts water,
4 x 4.25 in., Toho Eiga, 1990s (Figure 6-1) . . $20-28

Ash tray, ceramic Godzilla figural, smoke comes
out of mouth, 3.75 in., Toho Eiga, 1990s
(Figure 6-2) 12-20

Ash tray, Godzilla, ceramic, mountain base, 4.25 x
3.75 in., Toho Eiga, 1990s (Figure 6-3) 20-25

Backpack, "Godzilla, King of the Monsters,"
color graphic, Toho, Imaginings 3, 1996
(Figure 6-4) 15-25

Bank, egg with Superdeformed Godzilla inside,
Concord 15-25

Bank, Godzilla figural with red trim paint,
Beetland, 1983 150-200

Bank, Godzilla figural, poseable, plastic,
Trendmasters, 1994 10-20

Bank, Superdeformed Godzilla, 11 in., Uni-fied,
marked, "Japan Only," 1996 (Figure 6-5) 75-100

Bank, Tokyo Giants Baseball Team, #55-Godzilla,
movable parts, 5.25 in., Bandai (Figure 6-6) . . . 15-25

Cereal bowl, shows Superdeformed Godzilla,
Concord 12-20

Cigarette lighter, Godzilla figural, metal, black or
charcoal color, 2.5 in., Beetland, 1980s
(Figure 6-7) 40-65

Cigarette lighter, metal with torch flame, eyes light
up, Chinese, unlicensed, 2.5 in., 1990s
(Figure 6-8) 25-35

Clip, Godzilla head figural, metal and plastic, with
note pad, 2-in. clip, Bandai, 1993 (Figure 6-9) . . 9-14

Clip set, three small Godzilla clips, with
note pad, 1.4-in. clip, Bandai, 1993, set
(Figure 6-10) 12-18

(Figure 6-2) Godzilla figural ash tray, smoke comes out of mouth.

Computer brush, 10.75 in., Yutaka, in poly bag,
1996 (Figure 6-11) $10-15

Cup, figural cup, Concord 12-20

Cup, Godzilla head mug, Concord 15-25

Fan, hand-held, *Godzilla vs. Destroyah* theater
promo, plastic, 6.5 in., Toho Video, 1995
(Figures 6-12, 6-13) 7-12

Halloween costume, Godzilla suit and plastic
mask, Ben Cooper, boxed, 1978 50-75

Key chain, bendable Godzilla figural,
Trendmasters, 1994 (Figure 6-14) 3-6

(Figure 6-1) Godzilla ash tray, squirts water.

(Figure 6-3) Godzilla ash tray, mountain base.

(Figure 6-4, right) "Godzilla, King of the Monsters" backpack.

Key chain, Superdeformed Godzilla, black hollow
plastic, 1.75 in., Concord (Figure 6-15) $4-8
Lamp, Godzilla figural blinking lamp, plastic with
red trim, Beetland, boxed, 1982 60-90
Motion detector, plush Godzilla, moves, 9.5 in.,
Takara, 1991 (Figures 6-16, 6-17) 40-65
Mug, ceramic figural, 5.75 in., Toho Eiga,
1990s (Figure 6-18) 20-25
Necklace, pewter Godzilla pendant, 1.5 in.,
no mark 10-15
Necklace, plastic Godzilla whistle pendant, 5 in.
(Figure 6-19) 8-12
Ornament, inflatable mini-Godzilla, 6.25 in.
(Figure 6-20) 8-15
Soap dish, ceramic, 5.25 x 3 in., Toho Eiga,
1994 (Figure 6-21) 20-28
Soap dish, plastic, sticks to wall, 5 x 4.25 in.,
Yutaka, 1993 (Figure 6-22) 20-30
Soap dispenser, ceramic Godzilla figural, 6.25 in.,
Toho Eiga, 1990s (Figure 6-23) 22-30
Sunglasses strap, character strap with tiny Godzilla
figure, nylon strap, 8-in. package (Figure 6-24) . . 4-6
T-shirt, black with pink glow, lavender letters,
1980s (Figure 6-25) 15-20
T-shirt, "all-over" print, green and white, 1990s
(Figure 6-26) 20-25

(Figure 6-5) Superdeformed Godzilla bank.

(Figure 6-6) Tokyo Giants Godzilla bank.

(Figure 6-7) Godzilla figural cigarette lighters.

GHIDRAH · GHIDORAH · KING GHIDORAH · MECHAGHIDORAH

MATANGO (ATTACK OF THE MUSHROOM PEOPLE)

MEGALON

MINYA

(Figure 6-8) Godzilla cigarette lighter, eyes light up.

RODAN

Bank, Rodan figural bank, "LitGodzi," pink vinyl,
  5 in., Concord, in plastic wrap, 1990s
  (Figure 6-39) $12-22
Cup, figural cup, Concord 12-20
Necklace, pewter Rodan pendant, 1.25 in.,
  no mark (Figure 6-40) 10-15

SPACE GODZILLA

Bank, Superdeformed Space Godzilla figural, vinyl,
  in plastic wrap, Concord, 5 in., Concord, 1990s
  (Figure 6-41) 12-22

GROUP SHOTS

Chopstick holders, five monsters, 7 x 2-in. box,
  Takara, 1991 (Figure 6-42) 12-22
Film crew jacket, *Godzilla vs. MechaGodzilla,* 40th
  Anniv., pearlescent pressed vinyl, 1993 150-250
Glue bottle, Godzilla vs. MechaGodzilla,
  3.75 in. (Figure 6-43) 2-5
School slip file, Godzilla vs. Space Godzilla,
  7.5 x 10.5 in., 1994 (Figure 6-44) 8-12
Shopping bag, Godzilla vs. MechaGodzilla,
  17.5 x 12.25 in., 1993 (Figure 6-45) 8-15

(Figure 6-9) Figural Godzilla clip.

(Figure 6-10) Clip set, three small Godzilla head-shaped clips.

128

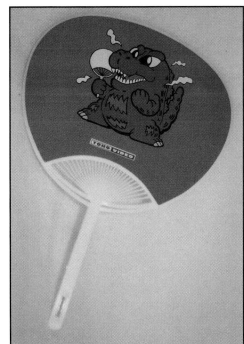

(Figure 6-45) Shopping bag, Godzilla vs. MechaGodzilla.

(Figure 6-13) Fan (back), Megalon, Godzilla, Godzilla Jr.

(Figure 6-12) Fan (front), Godzilla.

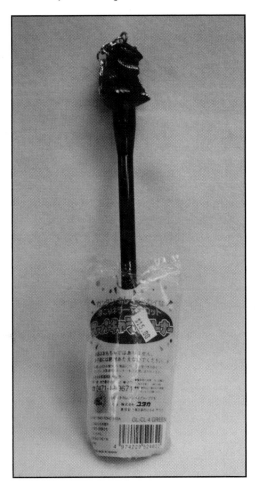

(Figure 6-11) Godzilla computer brush.

(Figure 6-14) Godzilla key chain.

(Figure 6-18) Ceramic mug.

(Figure 6-15) Superdeformed Godzilla key chain.

(Figure 6-16) Plush Godzilla motion detector.

(Figure 6-17) Plush Godzilla motion detector, box.

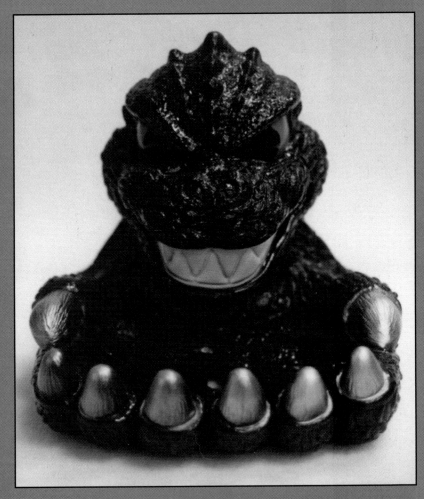

(Figure 6-22) Plastic soap dish.

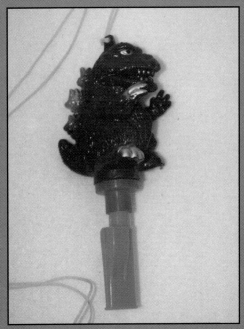

(Figure 6-19) Plastic whistle necklace.

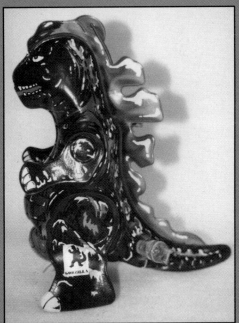

(Figure 6-20) Godzilla ornament.

(Figure 6-21) Ceramic soap dish.

(Figure 6-23) Godzilla figural soap dispenser.

(Figure 6-25) T-shirt, Godzilla with pink glow.

(Figure 6-26) T-shirt, "all-over" print.

(Figure 6-27) T-shirt, green Japanese writing.

(Figure 6-28) T-shirt, green glowing Godzilla.

(Figure 6-34) Godzilla window decal.

(Figure 6-24, right) Godzilla sunglasses strap.

(Figure 6-29) T-shirt, "United Nations Godzilla Countermeasure Center."

(Figure 6-30) Godzilla figural telephone rest.

(Figure 6-31) Godzilla tie pin.

(Figure 6-32) Godzilla figural toothbrush holder.

(Figure 6-35) Superdeformed Ghidrah figural bank.

(Figure 6-37) Megalon key chain.

(Figure 6-38) Minya key chain.

(Figure 6-42) Monster chopstick holders.

(Figure 6-33) Godzilla wall decoration.

(Figure 6-36) Matango necklaces.

(Figure 6-39) Superdeformed Rodan figural bank.

(Figure 6-41) Superdeformed Space Godzilla figural bank.

(Figure 6-40) Rodan necklace.

(Figure 6-43) Glue bottle,
Godzilla vs. MechaGodzilla.

(Figure 6-44) School slip
file, Godzilla vs. Space
Godzilla.

CHAPTER SEVEN
AMERICAN GODZILLA
1998

In 1995, Japan's Toho Studios killed off its star attraction, Godzilla, in *Godzilla vs. Destroyah*. The monster, however, did not actually die. Instead, his name and likeness were ushered off to America, to TriStar Pictures, in a special licensing arrangement.

At last, Americans who had grown up with Godzilla got the chance to make a new movie of their own, where Godzilla gets to attack New York. Okay—the experts in the audience will recall that Godzilla attacked New York in the 1960s feature, *Destroy All Monsters*, but this time we got a chance to use our own Hollywood magic to create a truly amazing Godzilla feature.

The childhood nostalgia factor drove many Godzilla fans into a frenzy of anticipation waiting for the new TriStar feature to be released. TriStar spent about $120 million on the film, directed by Roland Emmerich and produced by Dean Devlin, the dynamic duo responsible for the blockbuster *Independence Day*. TriStar also went to great lengths to keep Godzilla's new appearance a secret: top secret, until the day the film actually opened, May 19, 1998.

Godzilla's new look met with very mixed reviews, however, as those invested in childhood memories didn't recognize the monster at all. Those who had never seen a classic Godzilla film liked the monster just fine. But those who loved the old, foot-stomping, big-eyed monster who was obviously a guy in a suit . . . those people were, largely, disappointed.

The reason Godzilla looks different in the new American film is because Devlin and Emmerich also chose to re-write his origin. Like his namesake, the TriStar Godzilla was the product of atomic testing gone awry. But this time, the radiation didn't mutate and revive a dinosaur,

as in Toho's historical files. This time, the radiation mutated an average everyday marine iguana from French Polynesia.

When the gigantic lizard is ready to lay eggs, it heads for Manhattan, where, scientists reason, it's able to hide among the tall buildings. Along the way, it offs a few fishing boats (this is a classic Godzilla maneuver). Once in the Big Apple, Godzilla heads for the biggest, roundest, most nest-like building it can find—Madison Square Garden—and unloads about 200 eggs.

The eggs hatch and the film turns into a sort of *Jurassic Park* sequel, with hundreds of Baby Godzillas (roughly raptor-sized) chasing and attempting to eat the movie's stars.

Matthew Broderick takes on the role of the mild-mannered "worm guy," a scientist whose field of expertise is radiation's effects on small animals (specifically earthworms at Chernobyl). His real name is Dr. Tatopoulos, a tribute to Patrick Tatopoulos, the man responsible for designing the new Godzilla.

Broderick's love interest, a gutless, immoral wannabe TV reporter, is portrayed by Maria Pitillo. Her friend, a daring TV cameraman, Animal, is played by Hank Azaria.

While the scientists and reporters are trying to dig up more information on Godzilla, two government agencies are trying to put a stop to the monster's reign of destruction. The U.S. Military comes to aid New York with high-tech planes and plenty of troops, who, as in the classic Godzilla movies, prove virtually useless. There is also a secret French agency on hand, working undercover to help straighten out the mess, which they reason France caused by virtue of its atomic testing near Godzilla's point of origin. This group, which seems infinitely more clever than the U.S. troops, is led by Philippe Roache (Jean Reno).

The film advances through several false endings, until the real ending hits two hours and 18 minutes after the opening credits. Sequels had already been announced before the film was released (Broderick has signed for both), so it's no surprise the ending is left open. Although Godzilla is killed (once again) on the Brooklyn Bridge, one of its young survives.

AMERICAN GODZILLA COLLECTIBLES PRICE GUIDE
(ALL ITEMS 1998 UNLESS NOTED)

TOYS & FIGURES

Electronic Power Blast Godzilla, 10-in. figure,
   Toy Biz, 1998 . . . . $16-21
Godzilla Battle 8, electronic battle sound and
   action, 19 x 14-in. box, Toy Biz, 1998 22-32
Puppet, vinyl, with sound, glow-in-dark spines, ltd.ed.
   of 2500, 15 in., Resaurus, 1998 (Figure 7-1) . . 20-25
Remote Control Fast Attack Godzilla, 11-in. figure,
   Toy Biz, 1998 19-26
Remote Control Jaw Chomping Baby Godzilla,
   6-in. figure, Toy Biz, 1998 6-10

TRENDMASTERS TOYS

Action figure, Baby X, 5 in., Trendmasters,
   Baby Godzilla series, 1998 3-7
Action figure, Claw Slasher, 5 in., Trendmasters,
   Baby Godzilla series, 1998 (Figure 7-2) 3-7
Action figure, Hammer Foot, 5 in., Trendmasters,
   Baby Godzilla series, 1998 3-7
Action figure, Razor Fang, 5 in., Trendmasters,
   Baby Godzilla series, 1998 (Figure 7-3) 3-6
Action figure, Tail Thrasher, 5 in., Trendmasters,
   Baby Godzilla series, 1998 (Figure 7-4) 3-7
Action figure with Vehicle, Trendmasters, 1998,
   each 8-12
Combat Claw Godzilla, with electronic roar, 8 in.,
   Trendmasters, boxed, 1998 12-16
Fang Bite Godzilla, with electronic roar, 8 in.,
   Trendmasters, boxed, 1998 12-16
Hatchling figure, Hammer Tail with egg, 5 in.,
   Trendmasters, carded, 1998 7-11
Hatchling figure, Monster Claw with egg, 5 in.,
   Trendmasters, carded, 1998 7-11
Hatchling figure, Spike Jaw with egg, 5 in.,
   Trendmasters, carded, 1998 7-11

(Figure 7-1) Godzilla puppet with glow-in-the dark spines.

(Figure 7-2) Claw Slasher action figure.

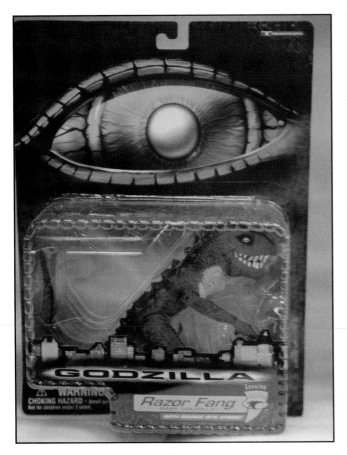

(Figure 7-4) Tail Thrasher
action figure.

(Figure 7-5) Sound Action
Godzilla.

(Figure 7-3) Razor Fang action figure.

(Figure 7-6) Ultimate Godzilla.

BOOKS, POSTERS, PAPER PRODUCTS AND CDS

CD, *Godzilla* soundtrack, Epic (Figure 7-7) $14-18

First showing packet, dated May 19, 1988, with ltd.
ed. film frame, coupons, cover (Figure 7-8) . . . 12-20

Movie poster, one-sheet, advance, black with
green logo, TriStar, 1998 15-25

Movie poster, Japanese version, 1998 15-25

Screenplay, *Godzilla* by Ted Elliott and Terry
Rossio, unused, Xeroxed, 1994 (Figure 7-9) . . $15-25

Stickers, value pack of 120, Mello Smello,
1998 (Figure 7-10) 2-3

Sticker album book, 14 pages, Mello Smello,
1998 (Figure 7-11) 4-5

Trading cards, Supervue, wide premium trading
cards, Inkworks, 1998, set (Figure 7-12) 10-20

Trading stickers, two-pack, Mello Smello, 1998 . . 1-1.50

CLOTHING AND ACCESSORIES

Pajamas, boy's size, two-piece, 100% cotton, shows
Godzilla on bridge 12-15

Shoes, kid's athletic shoes, Velcro strap 11-15

Shoes, kid's Godzilla sandals 9-12

(Figure 7-7) **Godzilla** *soundtrack, CD.*

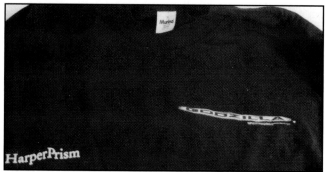

(Figure 7-13) Harper Prism book promo T-shirt.

(Figure 7-8) First showing packet.

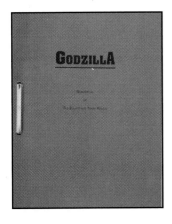

(Figure 7-9) Godzilla screenplay.

(Figure 7-11) Sticker album book.

(Figure 7-14) Godzilla backpack.

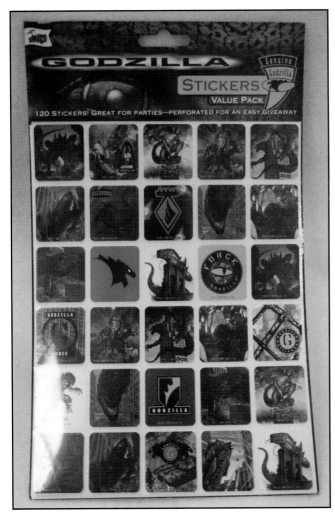

(Figure 7-10) Godzilla stickers.

(Figure 7-15) Birthday banner.

(Figure 7-12) Trading cards.

T-shirt, black with logo, Harper Prism book promo
distributed to book store employees only
(Figure 7-13) $25-40
T-shirt, child size, Godzilla underwater with
submarine, wrap design 7-10

HOUSEHOLD, SCHOOL, AND PARTY ITEMS

Backpack, cloth and vinyl, shows Godzilla
chomping a train (Figure 7-14) 8-15
Balloons, pack of six, 11 in., Creative Expressions . . 1-2
Birthday banner, jointed cardboard, 8.5 ft. long,
Creative Expressions (Figure 7-15) 2-4
Dreyer's Ltd. Ed. Godzilla Vanilla Ice Cream container,
half gallon with artwork (Figures 7-16, 7-17) 3-5
Gift Bag, 9.75 x 4.75 in., GGIL, 1998
(Figure 7-18) 1.50-2.00
Linens, comforter, twin size, blue with logo,
all-over design 28-35
Linens, twin size three-piece sheet set, blue with
logo, all-over design, polyester-cotton 15-18
Lunch bag, insulated, reusable lunch bag, Thermos
Company (Figure 7-19) 6-12
Lunch box, metal with designs on each side, plastic
thermos, Thermos Company (Figure 7-20) 6-12
Lunch box, blue plastic, thermos (Figure 7-21) . . . 5-10
Napkins, pack of sixteen large paper napkins,
Creative Expressions, 1998 (Figure 7-22) 1-2

(Figure 7-16) Dreyer's
Godzilla Vanilla Ice
Cream container (front).

(Figure 7-17) Dreyer's
Godzilla Vanilla Ice
Cream container (back).

Napkins, pack of sixteen small paper napkins,
Creative Expressions, 1998 (Figure 7-22) $1-2
Paper plates, eight-pack of 8.75-inch plates,
full-color graphic, Creative Expressions, 1998
(Figure 7-23) 1-2
Paper plates, eight-pack of 7-inch plates,
full-color graphic, Creative Expressions, 1998
(Figure 7-23) 1-2
Party cups, package of 9-oz cups, Creative
Expressions, 1998 1-2
Party hats, pack of eight, Creative Expressions
(Figure 7-24) 1.50-2.00

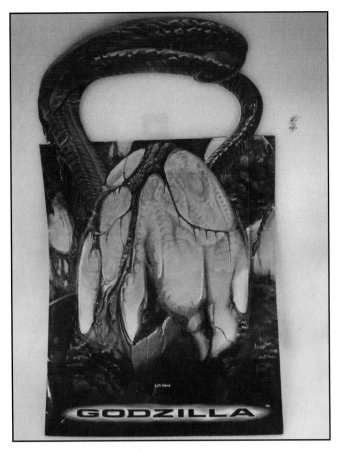

(Figure 7-18) Godzilla gift bag.

(Figure 7-19) Lunch bag.

(Figure 7-20) Metal lunch box.

(Figure 7-22) Two packs of paper napkins.

(Figure 7-21) Blue plastic lunch box.

(Figure 7-23) Two packs of paper plates.

(Figure 7-25) School folder.

(Figure 7-27) Godzilla table cover.

(Figure 7-26) Shopping bag.

(Figure 7-24) Godzilla party hats.

Pillow, Godzilla toss pillow, blue with logo and
all-over design $6-10
School folder, various designs with interior
pockets, cardboard (Figure 7-25) . . . . 50¢-1
Stadium cup, Creative Expressions, 1998 . . . . 50¢-1
Shaving kit, with razor, Godzilla figural razor
holder, shaving cream and brush 10-12
Shopping bag, black with logo and black string
handles, 12 x 15.5 in., 1997 (Figure 7-26) 3-5
Table cover, paper, 54 x 102 in.,
Creative Expressions (Figure 7-27) 2-3
"Thank You" notes, pack of eight with envelopes,
Creative Expressions, 1998 (Figure 7-28) 1-2
Tie pin, metal, promotional item, shows logo,
1998 (Figure 7-29) 3-5

TACO BELL ITEMS
Car cup holder, Godzilla figural, for sale only
at Taco Bell (Figure 7-30) 4-8
Cup, plastic, four designs with black plastic
lid, each (Figures 7-31—7-33) 2-4
Kid's Meal box, various designs, each (Figure 7-34) . 1-2
Kid's Meal premium, Hatchling in egg
key chain (Figure 7-35) 3-5
Kid's Meal premium, Godzilla figure 3-5
Kid's Meal premium, any other type 2-4
In-store Kid's Meal promo display 35-50
Staff member T-shirt with *Godzilla* promo 15-25

MISCELLANEOUS
Giant Duracell battery-automated Godzilla store
display, motorized cardboard, about
5 ft. tall 200-300
Store display, cardboard Godzilla head portrait
with raised logo, Target Stores (Figure 7-36) . . 20-35

(Figure 7-28) "Thank You" notes.

(Figure 7-29) Godzilla tie pin.

(Figure 7-30) Godzilla car cup holder.

(Figure 7-34) Kid's Meal box.

(Figure 7-35) Hatchling in egg key chain, Kid's Meal premium.

(Figure 7-31) Godzilla cup, Taco Bell premium.

(Figure 7-32) Godzilla cup, Taco Bell premium.

(Figure 7-36) Store display, Target stores.

(Figure 7-33) Godzilla cup, Taco Bell premium.

GAMERA

THE GUARDIAN OF THE UNIVERSE

CHAPTER EIGHT
GAMERA UNIVERSE

Gamera, a giant prehistoric turtle, was awakened from his icy Arctic tomb by atomic blasting in 1965. Upon his revival, Gamera made a beeline for Japan, where he soaked up energy and radiation from oil refineries and atomic research labs, mutating into the indestructible monster we all know and love—*Gamera, the Invincible.*

Initial attempts by the Japanese to stop Gamera failed, as they were only able to slow him down for a bit with freezing techniques. Finally, the U.S. came in to help, and the giant turtle was lured into a space ship and jettisoned toward Mars.

The following year, however, the rocket collided with a meteor and released Gamera, who flew back to earth! And Gamera's first sequel, *Gamera vs. Barugon*, was released to eager audiences. Barugon, another "re-activated" dinosaur, is rampaging through Japan after hatching from an opal discovered by treasure hunters. The two prehistoric behemoths meet and duke it out before Gamera wins and order is restored.

Gamera, now fully instated as a good guy, is next pitted against a blood-sucking, people-eating, giant bat-like creature called Gaos. Looking suspiciously like a second cousin of Godzilla's pal, Rodan, Gaos is armed with laser beam breath, tornado-force wing flaps, and fire-repellent jets in his chest. Gaos is awakened from his calm slumber in an ancient cave by an unwitting road construction crew. He gave Gamera a run for his money in 1967's *Gamera vs. Gaos*, and would return decades later, to seek vengeance for his defeat.

Gamera, now every child's best friend, takes on a monster threatening earth from outer space in his next assignment, *Gamera vs. Viras* (1968). When aliens from space land on earth, they enslave Gamera and force him to destroy cities. With the help of two boys, Gamera escapes, and it looks like the end of the alien threat, until they all merge and become one giant squid-like foe—Viras! In the end, however, Gamera saves the day.

The following year, Gamera takes off into space, to a planet just on the other side of the sun, where beautiful space women have kidnapped earth children with the express purpose of eating their brains! Gamera manages to save the day in *Gamera vs. Guiron*, even though he has to tangle with the evil, knife-headed monster, Guiron.

In 1970's *Gamera vs. Jiger*, Gamera defends the earth and the big Expo '70 against Jiger, a giant lizard-like monster. Jiger manages to pierce Gamera's chest plate, cutting him and knocking him out long enough to implant an egg inside the hero turtle. When the egg hatches inside Gamera, the baby Jiger sucks Gamera's blood, draining him of energy while big Jiger wreaks havoc. Luckily, two kids in a little submarine go inside Gamera's mouth (à la *Fantastic Voyage*), to remove the parasitic threat. People at Expo '70 and around the world cheer when the children succeed, and Gamera is victorious.

Gamera's final outing of his classic period takes place the following year, in *Gamera vs. Zigra*. Zigra, vaguely shark-like, flies to earth with a space ship full of aliens to take over the planet before it's destroyed by pollution. Zigra almost manages to kill Gamera, although the giant turtle is later revived by lightning during a storm. In the end, Zigra is no match for Gamera in this lackluster feature which marked the end of the series . . . for a while.

In 1979, Daiei tried to revive Gamera, with *Space Monster Gamera (Super Monster)*, an effort marked largely by spliced together old footage. This film features all of Gamera's old foes, and a new race of invading aliens, the

Zannons (whose ship looks amazingly like the Imperial Cruiser from *Star Wars*). This film borrowed not only from the old Gamera stock footage, but borrowed clips from *Space Cruiser Yamato* (*StarBlazers*) and *Galaxy Express 999* as well. Not a real crowd-pleaser, this film was first seen in the U.S. on MTV, oddly enough, way back in 1981.

In 1995, however, they got it right. This time, Gamera was back and better than ever. He's serious now, more muscular and much more adult, forced to battle three Gaos monsters in *Gamera, Guardian of the Universe*.

The following year, he was pitted against Legion, a monster rather like Godzilla's 1995 foe, Destroyah. Legion takes the form of many small bug-like creatures and one big crab-like creature in *Gamera 2: The Advent of Legion*, another crowd-pleaser.

Daiei Studios promises more Gamera movies soon! Initially a reaction to the popularity of Toho's Godzilla films, Gamera actually outranked the Big Guy in Japanese popularity polls for a while in the late 1960s. Although never as popular in America as Godzilla, Gamera's popularity is growing rapidly here, partially thanks to constant ribbing on TV's *Mystery Science Theater 3000*. Now, revived in the 1990s, he is a superstar in his own right, and some argue that *Gamera, Guardian of the Universe* outguns any of the recent Toho Godzilla efforts.

A great Gamera web site, "GamerAmerica" is online at http://members.aol.com/ungcc/colkco1.htm The site is operated by Mark Suggs of Denver, Colorado, who owns many of the high-end Gamera toys featured in this chapter.

GAMERA FILMOGRAPHY
DAIEI STUDIOS

1965 - GAMERA THE INVINCIBLE
Alternate titles: *Great Monster Gamera, Gammera the Invincible* (extra "m" in the U.S.)
U.S. Release Date: 1966
Monster Featured: Gamera

1966 - GAMERA VS. BARUGON
Alternate title: *War of the Monsters*
U.S. Release: TV only
Monsters Featured: Gamera, Barugon

1967 - GAMERA VS. GAOS
Alternate title: *Return of the Giant Monsters*
U.S. Release: TV only
Monsters Featured: Gamera, Gaos

1968 - GAMERA VS. VIRAS
Alternate title: *Destroy All Planets*
U.S. Release: TV only
Monsters Featured: Gamera, Viras

1969 - GAMERA VS. GUIRON
Alternate title: *Attack of the Monsters*
U.S. Release: TV only
Monsters Featured: Gamera, Guiron, Space Gaos

1970 - GAMERA VS. JIGER
Alternate title: *Gamera vs. Monster X*
U.S. Release: TV only
Monsters Featured: Gamera, Jiger

1971 - GAMERA VS. ZIGRA
U.S. Release: 1985 on USA Network
Monsters Featured: Gamera, Zigra

1979 - SPACE MONSTER GAMERA
Alternate Titles: *Super Monster, Super Monster Gamera*
U.S. Release: 1981 on MTV
Monsters Featured: Gamera, Gaos, Barugon, Viras, Guiron, Jiger, Zigra, and the Zannon invaders.

1995 - GAMERA, GUARDIAN OF THE UNIVERSE
U.S. Release: 1997, limited theatrical release
Monsters Featured: Gamera, Gaos

1996 - GAMERA 2: ADVENT OF LEGION
Alternate Title: *Gamera vs. Legion*
Monsters Featured: Gamera, Legion

FIGURES

BANDAI
GAMERA
Action figure, DX Gamera, metallic green paint
   on stomach, 11 in., 1996 (Figure 8-1) $50-75
Action figure, Gamera, old style, 7.25 in.,
   Bandai, 1991 (Figure 8-2) 100-150

(Figure 8-2) Gamera, 7.25 in., Bandai.

(Figure 8-5) Gamera 1996, Bandai.

(Figure 8-6) Plasma Gamera, Bandai.

(Figure 8-3) Gamera 1995, Bandai.

(Figure 8-7) Supersize Gamera, Bandai.

(Figure 8-1) DX Gamera, Bandai.

(Figure 8-8) Gamera, HG Gumball series, Bandai.

(Figure 8-4) Gamera 1995, blue vinyl, Bandai.

Action figure, Gamera 1995, 8 in., vinyl, Bandai,
   1995 (Figure 8-3) $25-35
Action figure, Gamera 1995, blue vinyl with
   white tusks, 4 in., Bandai, 1995 (Figure 8-4) . . . 5-10
Action figure, Gamera 1996, green opalescent
   plastic, 5.5 in., Bandai, 1996 (Figure 8-5) 25-35
Action figure, Plasma Gamera, ltd. ed., orange belly
   and feet, 6 in., Bandai, 1996 (Figure 8-6) 50-75
Action figure, Supersize Gamera, 12 in., Bandai,
   1995 (Figure 8-7) 110-135
Figure, Gamera, dark green plastic with cream
   accents, 4 in., HG Gumball series,
   1996 (Figure 8-8) 15-25
Miniature figure, Gamera 2, soft white plastic,
   1.25 in., Bandai, 1996 2-4

BARUGON

Action figure, Barugon, 3 in. tall, Bandai,
   1991 (Figure 8-9) 100-150
Action figure, Barugon, painted vinyl, 5.5 in.
   long with tongue, Bandai, 1995 (Figure 8-10) . . . 5-9
Miniature figure, Barugon, soft white plastic,
   2 in., Bandai, 1996 2-4

(Figure 8-9) Barugon, 3 in., Bandai.

GAOS

Action figure, Gaos, old style, 8 in., Bandai,
 1991 (Figure 8-11) $100-150
Action figure, Gaos 1995, red vinyl, 4 in., Bandai,
 1995 (Figure 8-12) 5-10
Action figure, Super Gaos, vinyl, 8 in., Bandai,
 1995 (Figure 8-13) 25-35
Figure, Gaos, 2.5 in., HG Gumball series,
 1995 (Figure 8-14) 15-25
Miniature figure, Gaos #1, blue-gray with pink on
 wings, 2.25 in., Bandai, 1995 (Figure 8-15) 4-8

(Figure 8-10) Barugon, 5.5 in., Bandai.

GUIRON

Action figure, Guiron, foe with knife head, plastic,
 4.5 in., Bandai, 1992 (Figure 8-16) 200-250
Figure, Gurion, 3.5 in., HG Gumball series,
 1996 (Figure 8-17) 15-25

LEGION

Action figure, Legion, 7 in., poseable, from *Gamera
 vs. Legion*, Bandai, 1996 (Figure 8-18) 30-50
Figure, Legion, 3 in., HG Gumball series,
 1996 (Figure 8-19) 5-25
Miniature figure, Legion, soft green plastic, 1.5 in.,
 Bandai, 1996 (Figure 8-20) 2-4

(Figure 8-14) Gaos, HG Gumball series, Bandai.

(Figure 8-11) Gaos, Bandai.

(Figure 8-12) Gaos 1995, Bandai.

(Figure 8-13) Super Gaos, Bandai.

(Figure 8-15) Miniature Gaos, 1.5 in., Bandai.

(Figure 8-16) Gurion, 4.5 in., Bandai.

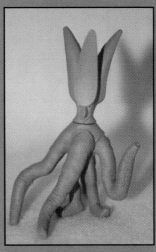

(Figure 8-21) Viras, HG
Gumball series, Bandai.

(Figure 8-17) Gurion, HG Gumball series, Bandai.

(Figure 8-18) Legion, Bandai.

(Figure 8-19) Legion, HG Gumball series, Bandai.

(Figure 8-20) Miniature Legion, 1.5 in.,
Bandai.

VIRAS

Figure, Viras, 3.5 in., HG Gumball series,
   1996 (Figure 8-21) $15-25

ZIGRA

Action figure, Zigra, plastic, 8 in., Bandai,
   1991 (Figure 8-22) 100-150
Miniature figure, Zigra, soft green plastic,
   1.5 in., Bandai, 1996 (Figure 8-23) 2-4

M1

GAMERA

Figure, Gamera, vinyl, green with pink and black
   paint, 10.5 in., in poly bag, 1996
   (Figure 8-24) $30-60
Figure, Gamera, vinyl, Plasma version, 10 in.,
   in poly bag, 1996 30-60

MARMIT

GAMERA

Action figure, Gamera, 10 in., Marmit, Vinyl Paradise
   series, in poly bag, 1997 (Figure 8-25) 35-70
Action figure, Gamera, 10 in., Marmit, Vinyl Paradise
   series, Gamera vs. Jiger version, 1998 35-70
Action figure, Gamera, dark blue vinyl, 9 in.,
   Marmit, 1996 35-70

BARUGON

Action figure, Barugon, 4 in. tall, Marmit, Vinyl
   Paradise series, 1997 (Figure 8-26) 35-70

(Figure 8-22) Zigra, 8 in., Bandai.

(Figure 8-23) Miniature Zigra, 1.5 in., Bandai.

(Figure 8-24) Gamera, green with pink and black paint, M1.

(Figure 8-25) Gamera, Vinyl Paradise series, Marmit.

GAOS · SPACE GAOS

Action figure, Gaos, 10 in., Marmit, Vinyl
Paradise series, in poly bag, 1997 . . . . $35-70
Action figure, Space Gaos, Marmit, Vinyl
Paradise series, 1997 60-90

GUIRON

Action figure, Guiron, Marmit, Vinyl Paradise
series, in poly bag, 1997 35-70

JIGER

Action figure, Jiger, 5 in. tall, Marmit, Vinyl
Paradise series, 1998 (Figure 8-27) 35-70

VIRAS

Action figure, Viras, white with silver, 11.25 in.,
Marmit, Vinyl Paradise series, 1997
(Figure 8-28) 35-70

ZIGRA

Action figure, Zigra, 10 in., Marmit, Vinyl Paradise
series, 1997 35-70

MARUSAN

GAOS

Figure, Gaos, turquoise vinyl, 5.5 in., Marusan,
1967 (Figure 8-29) 2,000-2,500

(Figure 8-26) Barugon, Vinyl Paradise series, Marmit.

(Figure 8-27) Jiger, Vinyl Paradise series, Marmit.

(Figure 8-29) Gaos, turquoise vinyl, Marusan.

NITTO

GAMERA

Figure, Gamera, hollow vinyl, green and gold,
   4 in., Nitto, medium-sized series,
   1970-1971 (Figure 8-30) $500-600
Figure, Gamera, bright green vinyl, white teeth,
   5 in., Nitto, Kawada series, 1978
   (Figure 8-31) 200-250

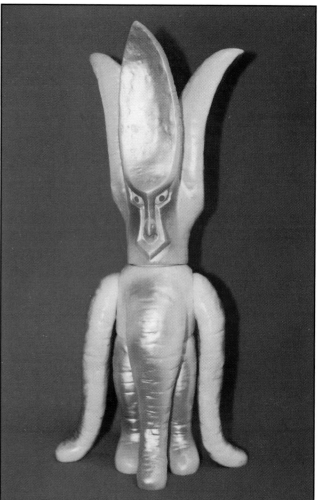

(Figure 8-28) Viras, Vinyl Paradise series, Marmit.

BARUGON

Figure, Barugon, "Begging Puppy" Barugon,
   hollow vinyl, 8.25 in., standard size, Nitto,
   1970-1971 (Figure 8-32) $200-275
Figure, Barugon, brown and green, vinyl,
   4.25 in. tall, Nitto, Kawada series, 1978
   (Figure 8-33) 200-250

GAOS

Figure, Gaos, hollow vinyl, brick red, 4 in., Nitto,
   medium-sized series, 1970-1971
   (Figure 8-34) 300-400
Figure, Gaos, hollow vinyl, 3 in., Nitto, mini
   series, 1970-1971 (Figure 8-35) 300-400

GUIRON

Figure, Guiron, hollow vinyl, 4 in., Nitto, mini
   series, 1970-1971 (Figure 8-36) 750-1,000

(Figure 8-30) Gamera, hollow green and gold vinyl, Nitto.

(Figure 8-35) Gaos, mini series, 3 in., Nitto.

(Figure 8-31) Gamera, Kawada series, Nitto.

(Figure 8-33) Barugon, Kawada series, Nitto.

(Figure 8-32) "Begging Puppy" Barugon, Nitto.

(Figure 8-34) Gaos, 4 in., Nitto.

(Figure 8-36) Gurion, hollow vinyl, Nitto.

(Figure 8-38) Jiger, 4 in., Nitto.

(Figure 8-40) Zigra, white head, Nitto.

(Figure 8-37) Jiger, mini series, 3 in., Nitto.

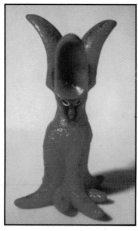

(Figure 8-39) Viras, 8 in., Nitto.

JIGER

Figure, Jiger, hollow yellow vinyl, 3 in., Nitto,
   mini series, 1970-1971 (Figure 8-37) $300-400
Figure, Jiger, hollow vinyl, orange and silver,
   4 in., standard size, Nitto, 1970-1971
   (Figure 8-38) 150-200

VIRAS

Figure, Viras, 8 in., standard size, hollow red
   vinyl, Nitto, 1970-1971 (Figure 8-39) 200-275

(Figure 8-41) Zigra, mini series, 3 in., Nitto.

(Figure 8-42) Zigra, silver or dark blue head, Nitto.

(Figure 8-44) Legion, 6 in., Yutaka.

ZIGRA

Figure, Zigra, hollow vinyl, white head, 4.5 in., Nitto, medium-sized series, 1970-1971 (Figure 8-40)...................... $500-600

Figure, Zigra, hollow vinyl, blue and silver, 3 in., Nitto, mini series, 1970-1971 (Figure 8-41) 300-400

Figure, Zigra, hollow vinyl, silver or dark blue head, 8.5 in., standard size, Nitto, 1970-1971 (Figure 8-42) 200-275

YAMAKATSU

GAMERA

Figure, Gamera, solid dark brown rubber, 3 in., Japanese trading card premium, 1979 (Figure 8-43) 125-175

GAOS

Figure, Gaos, solid rubber, 3 in., Japanese trading card premium, 1979 125-175

YUTAKA

GAMERA

Action figure, Gamera, 6 in., Yutaka, 1995 10-15

Action figure, Gamera, green with light green on back, 5.75 in., Yutaka, 1996 10-15

GAOS

Action figure, Gaos, 6 in., Yutaka, 1995 10-15

LEGION

Action figure, Legion, 6 in., Yutaka, 1996 (Figure 8-44) 10-15

(Figure 8-43) Gamera, Japanese trading card premium, Yamakatsu.

UNLICENSED, UNKNOWN, NO MARK
OTHERS
Action figure, Gaos, 4 in., hollow plastic, Japanese
(Figure 8-45) $8-12

GAMERA MOVIE POSTERS, FILM, VIDEO, AND THEATER MATERIAL
GAMERA THE INVINCIBLE
GAMMERA THE INVINCIBLE (RELEASED IN U.S. WITH AN EXTRA "M")
Movie poster, *Gamera the Invincible*, 1966,
Japanese version 600-750
Movie poster, *Gammera the Invincible*, 1965,
U.S. version 75-150

Video, *Gamera the Invincible*, Japanese, Daiei
Video Museum, 1965 (Figure 8-46) $40-55

GAMERA VS. BARUGON
Movie poster, *Gamera vs. Barugon*, 1966,
Japanese 400-500

GAMERA VS. GAOS
Movie poster, *Gamera vs. Gaos*, 1967,
Japanese 500-600

GAMERA VS. VIRAS
Movie poster, *Gamera vs. Viras*, 1968,
Japanese 350-450

(Figure 8-45) Gaos action figure, Japanese.

(Figure 8-46) Video, Gamera the Invincible.

(Figure 8-47) Movie poster, Gamera, Guardian of the Universe.

(Figure 8-48) Program, Gamera, Guardian of the Universe.

GAMERA VS. GUIRON
Movie poster, *Gamera vs. Guiron*, 1969,
    Japanese $200-300

GAMERA VS. JIGER
Movie poster, *Gamera vs. Jiger*, 1970, Japanese . 150-250

GAMERA VS. ZIGRA
Movie poster, *Gamera vs. Zigra*, 1971,
    Japanese 150-250

SPACE MONSTER GAMERA (SUPER MONSTER)
Movie poster, *Space Monster Gamera*, version A or B,
    1979, Japanese 75-150

GAMERA, GUARDIAN OF THE UNIVERSE
Movie poster, *Gamera, Guardian of the Universe*,
    Japanese version, 1995 (Figure 8-47) 25-40
Program, *Gamera, Guardian of the Universe*,
    11.75 x 8.25 in., 1995 (Figure 8-48) 15-25

Video, *Gamera, Guardian of the Universe*, Daiei,
    Japanese, 1995 (Figure 8-49) $40-55
Video, *The Making of Gamera*, Daiei, Japanese,
    1996 (Figure 8-50) 25-35

GAMERA 2
Movie poster, *Gamera 2*, Japanese version,
    1996 (Figure 8-51) 25-40
Program, *Gamera 2*, 11.75 x 8.25 in.,
    1996 (Figure 8-52) 15-25
Video, *Gamera 2, Gamera vs. Legion*, Daiei,
    Japanese, 1996 (Figure 8-53) 40-55

MODEL KITS
GAMERA
Model kit, Gamera, 1/450 scale, plastic, ARII . . . 12-20
Model kit, Gamera, 1/350 scale, plastic, 10.75 x
    6.75-in. box with volcano art (Figure 8-54) . . . 12-20
Model kit, Gamera, flying, vinyl, M-1
    (Figure 8-55) 165-225

(Figure 8-49) Video, Gamera, Guardian of the Universe.

(Figure 8-50) Video, The Making of Gamera.

(Figure 8-53, right) Video, Gamera 2.

(Figure 8-51) Movie poster, Gamera 2.

(Figure 8-52) Program, Gamera 2.

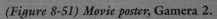

(Figure 8-56) Four Nitto Mascot series model kits. Clockwise from top left: Gamera, Gaos, Gappa, Barugon.

Model kit, Gamera, Nitto, Mascot series, 3.75 x
7-in. box, 1971-1972 (Figure 8-56) $300-400

Model kit, Gamera 1995, 1/250 scale, soft
vinyl, Falchion 100-150

Model kit, Gamera 1995, resin, Volks 100-150

Model kit, Gamera 1996 standing, 1/250th scale,
soft vinyl, Tsukuda Hobby 75-100

Model kit, Gamera 1996 flying, 1/250th scale,
soft vinyl, Tsukuda Hobby 75-100

BARUGON

Model kit, Barugon, Nitto, Mascot series, 3.75 x
7-in. box 1971-1972 (Figure 8-56) 300-400

GAOS

Model kit, Gaos, Mascot series, 3.75 x 7- in. box,
Nitto, 1971-1972 (Figure 8-56) 300-400

Model kit, Gaos II 1995, resin, Volks 150-175

LEGION

Model kit, Legion Soldier, 1/250 scale, soft vinyl,
Tsukuda Hobby 75-100

TOYS

Battery-op Gamera, Bandai, Real Hobby Series,
boxed 200-275

Battery-op Plasma Walk Gamera, walks, roars,
10 in., Bandai 100-125

Battle set, with 4-in. Gamera, Super Gaos and
Tokyo tower, Bandai, 1995 40-50

*(Figure 8-54) Gamera
model kit.*

(Figure 8-55) Flying Gamera model kit.

Carnival playset, with seven 4-in. Gamera monsters
and Tokyo tower, Bandai, 1995 . . . . $40-50
Gamera DX, electronic toy with sound, 8 in.,
Bandai, 1996 (Figure 8-57) 75-100
Gamera vs. Legion, boxed set of action figures,
Bandai, 1996 (Figure 8-58) 25-40
Puzzle, Gamera vs. Gaos, frame tray, 15 x 12.5 in.,
Epoch, in poly bag, 1970s (Figure 8-59) . . . 100-150

BOOKS, MAGAZINES, CARDS, AND PAPER

G-Fan magazine, #14, Gamera fights Godzilla on
cover, Mar./Apr. 1995 15-25
G-Fan magazine, #22, Gamera on cover, Jul./Aug.
1996 (Figure 8-60) 5-8
Monster Times cover story, Gamera, issue #37,
1970s 7-10

(Figure 8-57) Gamera DX, electronic toy with sound.

(Figure 8-59, left) Gamera vs. Gaos puzzle.

(Figure 8-58) Gamera vs. Legion, boxed set of action figures.

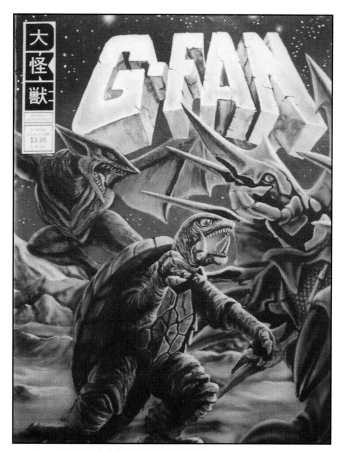

(Figure 8-60) G-Fan *magazine #22.*

(Figure 8-61) Book, Daiei Special Effect Movies.

(Figure 8-62) Book, Gamera Chronicles:
**The History of Daiei Fantastic Movies,
1942-1996.**

MISCELLANEOUS

Key chain, Gamera, soft vinyl, Showa Note, Japan,
1995 . . . . $8-12
Key chain, Gaos, soft vinyl, Showa Note, Japan,
1995 (Figure 8-65) 8-12
Key chain, Gaos, figural (Figure 8-66) 8-12
T-shirt, Gamera 2, black with pocket logo, back
design, sold only in Japanese theaters, 1996 . . . 50-65
Tie pin, Gamera, plastic, 0.875 in., Showa Note,
1996 (Figure 8-67) .7-12

(Figure 8-65) Gaos key chain, soft vinyl.

(Figure 8-66) Gaos figural key chain.

(Figure 8-64) Book, **Gamera 2.**

(Figure 8-63) Book, **Gamera, Guardian of the Universe.**

(Figure 8-67) **Gamera 2** *tie pin.*

Haruo Nakajima, the man who wore the Godzilla suit from 1954 until 1972, was a special guest of honor at G-Con 1998. Here, he strikes a heroic monster pose in front of a toy spread in the Dealers Room.

CHAPTER NINE
G-FANDOM

Fans and collectors of Godzilla, Gamera, and other Japanese monsters have become somewhat organized in the United States and abroad. There are currently two annual conventions hosted each year to celebrate Godzilla, as well as a few regularly published fan magazines.

In late 1996, the core organizers of U.S. Godzilla fandom had a parting of the ways, but, luckily, instead of the separation putting an end to the activities and publications, it doubled them. There are now two conventions each year in Chicago and two really decent fanzines.

Connecting with other fans and collectors is what really makes the hobby fun and exciting. We heartily recommend linking up with "others of your own kind," via these avenues:

G-CON

Annual convention in Chicago
hosted by Daikaiju Productions
890 E. 14th Street, Suite 4B
Brooklyn, New York 11230
718/253-8649
head honcho: John Roberto

The 1998 G-Con boasted about 650 attendees from across the country and beyond. In addition to hundreds of interesting fans, the convention featured some very special guests: Haruo Nakajima, the man who actually wore the Godzilla suit from 1954 to 1972, and Kenpachiro Satsuma, the man who wore the suit from 1984 to 1995. Also imported from Japan was Yoshio Tsuchiya, the infamous "Controller from Planet X" in five Godzilla films.

One of the big draws of G-Con is the Dealers' Room, packed with a plethora of amazing collectibles and toys from several importers and dealers from around the country.

Another highlight is the costume contest Saturday night. In 1998, the contest included amazing depictions of Mothra, Godzilla, and MechaGodzilla, with some others thrown in for fun.

Panel discussions, a model building contest, a live band (yes, they covered the Blue Oyster Cult song) and good parties round out the activities.

G-FEST

Annual convention in Chicago
hosted by Daikaiju Enterprises
Box 3468
Steinbach, Manitoba
Canada, R0A 2A0
head honcho: J.D. Lees

G-Fest features an art contest, model contest, costume contest, amateur video contest, trivia contest, coloring contest, and even a monster-voice impression contest.

For those less competitive, there's a Dealers Room, loads of panel discussions, guest experts, game playing, and more! A great way to spend a weekend.

G-FAN MAGAZINE

Published every other month by J.D. Lees, Box 3468, Steinbach, Manitoba, Canada, R0A 2A0. See Chapter 5 for complete listings.

KAIJU FAN MAGAZINE

Published quarterly by John Roberto, 890 East 14th St., Suite 4B, Brooklyn, New York 11230. See Chapter 5 for complete listings.

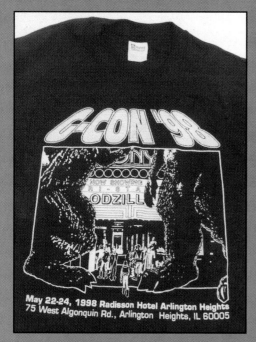

The official commemorative G-Con '98 T-shirt carefully avoids copyright infringement, as it indicates the new TriStar movie is afoot.

Godzilla was ready to greet attendees in the Radisson lobby at G-Con '98. The man who designed and wore the suit is Dennis Lanncaster.

Not everyone at the convention enjoyed the new TriStar movie, however, as this fan (Tom Rohden of Crystal Lake, Illinois), demonstrates with his home-made anti-Dean Devlin T-shirt.

A highlight of Saturday night's costume contest was Mothra (who shot silly string from its moving mandibles). Dennis Lanncaster created the incredible suit!

172

Kenpachiro Satsuma, who wore the Godzilla suit in Toho's later movies, 1984-1995, was also on hand.

Paul Gairns of Baltimore said it took about two or three months to make this astounding MechaGodzilla '74 costume.

The Dealers Room was packed with luscious collectibles, brought by dealers from around the country.

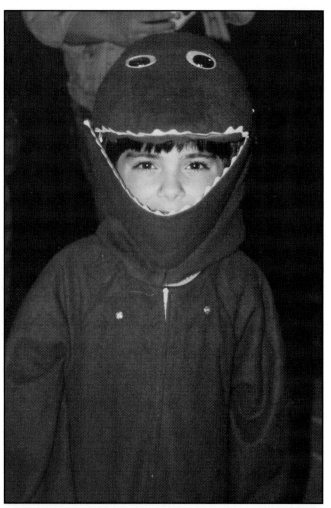

Mothra and a rubber-suited Godzilla battle in the lobby of the Radisson!

(Right) Young Ian Nixon portrayed the son of Godzilla in this great Minya outfit.

Dennis Lancaster's Mothra roamed the floor, gaining lots of attention from fans at G-Con '98.

ABOUT THE AUTHOR

Dana Cain has loved Japanese Movie Monsters since the early 1960s, when she first saw *King Kong vs. Godzilla* at the Okla Theater in McAlester, Oklahoma. A collector of Japanese monsters for more than 10 years, and a professional writer for more than 20 years, Dana is the author of *Film & TV Animal Star Collectibles* and *Collecting Monsters of Film and TV*. She now lives in Denver, Colorado.

Dana helped found Atomic Antiques and the Collector's Supershow, both located in Denver. A graduate of the Missouri Auction School, she also hosts the Rocky Mountain Toy Auction.

When she's not working with collectibles, Dana enjoys painting, reading tarot cards and teaching the Enneagram.

Her personal collections include: Godzilla, Lassie, Flipper, Benji, horses, 101 Dalmations, old dog prints and photos, jackalopes, religious artifacts, modern art and sock monkeys.